CREATING A
Sexually Healthy
NATION

CELEBRATING 100 YEARS OF THE
AMERICAN SEXUAL HEALTH ASSOCIATION

STRANGE FRUIT
Honest, caring, BiWM, Br/Br, 24, 6',
N-S/D taoist, vegetarian. Interests:
writing, running, literature, nature,
cinema, science fiction, arcades,
penguins, comic books. ISO relationship. POB 5821, Raleigh
27650-5821. CALL #6057 ☎

CONTENTS

Sexual Health—An Ever-Evolving Concept EDWARD W. HOOK III, MD

EDWARD (NED) W. HOOK III, MD, is the director of the Division of Infectious Diseases and a Professor of Medicine, Epidemiology and Microbiology at the University of Alabama at Birmingham. Ned is also a former chairman of the board for ASHA.

WHEN ASKED TO WRITE THE FOREWORD to this volume, I readily agreed. What better way would there be to start ASHA's second 100 years than to consider the many facets of sexual health through personal stories, describing how some aspect of sexual health and sexuality has impacted individuals in their work, their lives, and their interactions with others? I was anxious to see what topics the authors we approached would choose and how they would narrow down 100 years into just a few paragraphs. As expected, I found many differing perspectives, but one common theme struck me as I read through the essays—change. In some way almost all of the entries have to do with changes—historical changes, political changes, societal changes, scientific changes, personal changes, changes in visions for the future—as they relate to some element of sexuality and sexual health. Certainly there has been great change during the century in which the American Social Hygiene-Social Health-Sexual Health Association has worked to improve sexual health in this country. (The name changes alone are telling.) As I continued to read the essays we had collected, I began to wonder how I had changed since I started doing this work.

My own personal story of change was stimulated by the privilege of being chosen to give the lecture that accompanies receipt of the American Sexually Transmitted Diseases Association's Thomas Parran Award in 2008. At that time, having spent more than 25 years as an investigator and clinician focused on the management and prevention of sexually transmitted infections (STIs), I was frustrated that our efforts had not reaped larger benefits. I found myself pondering why, as a nation, we couldn't do better in terms of STI control. It wasn't for lack of knowledge, tools, or effort. We already knew so much about the epidemiology of STIs; there were accurate, easily used, and rapidly evolving tools for STI diagnosis; we had highly effective therapy that could cure bacterial STIs; and we were even able to help reduce transmission of viral STIs. Moreover, we were spending large amounts of money. Despite all of the knowledge and resources, however, our nation was not even doing as well at STI control as most other developed nations.

My reflections led me to believe that one important contributor to our nation's limited success in addressing STIs was the widespread stigmatization relating to sex and sexuality, particularly as it impacted health-promoting behaviors. It seemed that all too often not just STIs but sex itself was treated as a stigma-laden topic that was not acceptable for discussion. It seemed that, driven by this stigma, our nation had developed a paradoxical outlook toward sexuality in which while manifestations of sexuality were widespread throughout popular culture, the same topics were somehow not acceptable for serious discussions, even between partners or in the context of health care.

I realized that before we could address S T I control, we would have to sort out how to encourage discussions about sex and sexuality without embarrassment or reticence. Perhaps we needed to move away from the traditional, loss-frame focus on diseases and the untoward consequences of sexuality and shift the focus toward the positive, gain-frame goal of sexual health, starting with acknowledgement that this is a normal and appropriate topic for discussion.

As my own perspective evolved, my thinking was shaped by counsel I once received and have never forgotten: to bring about change, it is less important to be able to articulate the reasons why change might be for the good than to understand and be prepared to counter opposition to proposed changes. I recognized that unless we understood the barriers to these changes, accomplishing them was going to be very difficult. For sexual health, I believe the largest barrier is the basic embarrassment we have in acknowledging ourselves (and our parents, friends, and children) as sexual beings.

Since this epiphany, my personal efforts to adopt a sexual health perspective have led me to make adjustments in how I speak with patients, colleagues, and even friends. In my interactions—be they professional or personal—I try to decrease focus on disease and stigma, relieve embarrassment, and concentrate on the benefits of sexual health. I hope this volume will help others do the same.

This collection of essays not only celebrates 100 years of change and evolution for A S H A, it also provides many powerful and often personal messages of change. We believe these essays will stimulate reflection, provide new insights, and most importantly, spur even more positive change.

IS *YOUR* MIND DISEASED?

SOCIAL HYGIENE DIVISION ARMY EDUCATIONAL COMMISSION

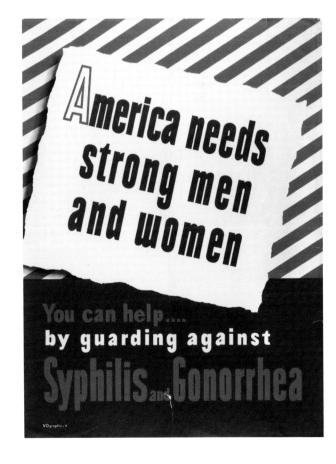

America needs strong men and women

You can help....
by guarding against
Syphilis and Gonorrhea

Early History of ASHA LINNEA M. ANDERSON, MA

LINNEA M. ANDERSON, MA, is the archivist in the Social Welfare History Archives at the University of Minnesota. She received an MA in History and Certificate in Archival Management from New York University in 1993 and a BA in History and Theatre from St. Olaf College in Northfield, Minnesota in 1987.

THE CARTOON ON THIS PAGE CAPTURES THE GOALS of the American Sexual Health Association's (ASHA) early history and some of the core methods and ideas that informed its early work: the importance of education, medical research, and treatment in the fight against sexually transmitted infections (STIs) and an attack on the cultural myths and "false modesty" that allowed STIs to spread. Researching ASHA's history using its archival records provides an up-close view of the past though items such as this cartoon and the hundreds of thousands of letters, reports, posters, pamphlets, and other documents in the ASHA files. The Social Welfare History Archives at the University of Minnesota houses more than 100 feet of records that document ASHA's predecessors in the early 1900s, its founding, and its first 90 years as the American Social Hygiene Association and the American Social Health Association. The records are an important part of the story of public health and social reform in the 20th century.

From our current vantage point in the early 21st century, it is sometimes difficult to grasp the groundbreaking nature of ASHA's early work and to see past perspectives and language of 100 years ago. Looking back at the history of ASHA through its archival records highlights many important differences and advancements over time. However, it also shows that common concerns and themes remain: the importance of accurate sexual health information; open discussion of sexual health topics; and a collaborative responsibility for personal and public health shared by the individual, society, and the community of health, social service, public policy, and education professionals.

ASHA's many activities and accomplishments in its first 100 years cannot be covered in a single essay. In recognition of ASHA's centennial, this essay focuses on the founding and early history of the organization and briefly discusses its work up to the mid-1940s, when the availability of penicillin changed the terms of the fight against STIs. It outlines important themes and goals of ASHA's early decades and describes some programs that exemplify them, many of which continue today, albeit in different forms.

"If We Can Get The Beast Out Of His Lair We'll Win the Fight" A promotional cartoon drawn for the first National Social Hygiene Day in 1937 by Harry E. Larimer.

THE FOUNDING

ASHA was formed by the consolidation of organizations fighting against prostitution, trafficking, and STIs, known at the time as "venereal diseases." The American Social Hygiene Association had roots in two important reform movements of the 19th and early 20th centuries: the health and sanitary reform movement and the "social protection" and anti-prostitution movement. Both outlooks influenced ASHA's early work. In *No Magic Bullet: A Social History of Venereal Disease in the United States since 1880*, Allan Brandt explains: "Social hygiene drew together two prominent Progressive contingents: those demanding a homogeneous moral order and those dedicated to a new scientific, technocratic vision. The social hygiene campaign, committed both to health *and* sexual morality, attempted to negotiate the inherent conflict between these emphases."[1]

ASHA's anti-prostitution, social protection roots came from two organizations: The American Purity Alliance and The National Vigilance Committee. The American Purity Alliance was incorporated in 1895. Its predecessor, the New York Committee for the Prevention of State Regulation of Vice, was founded in 1876. The Alliance advocated legal protection for underage women against prostitution and giving "aid and encouragement in the way of securing victims of social vice and in providing them with suitable homes and employment." The National Vigilance Committee was formed in 1906 to fight for "constant, persistent and absolute repression of prostitution," the "rescue and protection" of girls and women, and to promote knowledge of the "social evil" (a contemporary term for prostitution). These merged in 1912 to form The American Vigilance Association.

ASHA's more progressive, sexual health origins came from the American Federation for Sex Hygiene, which was founded in 1910 and incorporated in 1912. The Federation advocated educating the public about the "physiology and hygiene of sex" and preventing STIs and prostitution though "sanitary, moral and legislative" means.

Another organization, The American Society for Sanitary and Moral Prophylaxis, which was founded in 1905 by Prince Morrow, eventually merged with ASHA in 1918. Morrow, a physician-turned-reformer, had been strongly influenced by the 1902 Congress on International Traffic in Women and Children in Brussels. He re-

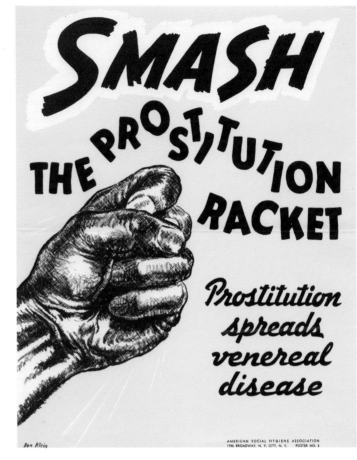

SMASH THE PROSTITUTION RACKET

Prostitution spreads venereal disease

Ben Klein

AMERICAN SOCIAL HYGIENE ASSOCIATION
1790 BROADWAY, N. Y. CITY, N. Y.   POSTER NO. 5

turned to the United States inspired to combat prostitution with a combined educational and moral campaign. Although Morrow died in 1913, he was an important influence on ASHA's combined focus on educational, "sanitary," and regulatory tactics.

Following Morrow's death, hygiene and anti-prostitution movement supporters John D. Rockefeller Jr. and Grace H. Dodge urged these disparate organizations to form one national group. There had already been some discussion and tension around the issue of whether the groups should join forces, and the intervention of these two important donors helped tip the balance towards a merger. Starting between 1910 and 1913, ASHA's archival records reveal discussions of a possible merger among the many interested parties in the fight against prostitution and STIs.

The International Congress of School Hygiene held in Buffalo, New York, in August 1913 brought together many key figures in these movements. At the conference, the American Vigilance Association and the American Federation for Sex Hygiene agreed to merge. Minutes of American Federation for Sex Hygiene's August 27, 1913 meeting at International Congress contain a resolution "...to unite with the American Vigilance Association....and to be hereafter known as the American Sex Hygiene and Vigilance Association." This early name was quickly dropped in favor of "American Social Hygiene Association."

The October 23, 1913 minutes of the American Federation for Sex Hygiene discuss a proposed constitution for the "American Social Hygiene Association," possibly the first mention of the ASHA name. At a special meeting of the Federation on December 3, 1913, the board and executive committee voted to adopt a new constitution and bylaws and set April 1st as the official date for the merger. On January 21, 1914 the certificate of incorporation was signed by Donald R. Hooker, Delcevare King, Robert W. Hebberd, Thomas M. Balliet, Edward L. Keyes Jr., Thomas N. Hepburn, William Freeman Snow, and James B. Reynolds. The new association was publicly announced on Valentine's Day, 1914.

ASHA's constitution stated that it would "promote social health;" "advocate the highest standards of private and public morality;" "suppress commercialized vice;" defend the community against STIs through "education, sanitary or legislative" means; investigate "prostitution and the venereal diseases in American towns and cities;" and promote cooperation between local organizations to support this work. This revised version of the constitution had a slightly more progressive and scientific tone than the one proposed at the International Congress in 1913. In particular, investigation plays a key role in the program and replaces the "social protection" language of the original document. Research and investigation as well as education became cornerstones of the ASHA's program.

ASHA's new co-executives were James B. Reynolds, a lawyer from the National Vigilance Committee, and William Freeman Snow, professor of public health at Stanford University. In 1914, ASHA had two departments: the Legal Department, headed by Reynolds, and the Education Department, headed by Snow. Its main office was in New York City with branch offices in Chicago and San Francisco. By 1915, it also had a Department of Investigation headed George J. Kneeland. This department also employed investigators (including women) as needed.

ASHA'S EARLY WORK

ASHA's core goals and messages in its early decades reflect the sometimes competing, sometimes complimentary goals of both the Progressive Era reformers and the purity and vigilance movements. ASHA's first annual report in 1914 outlines a more progressive method of approaching social problems "not after the manner of impulsive and superficial sentimentalists, but in the spirit and with the methods of modern science, education, and enlightened morality" and to "unite intelligent men and women throughout our country who abhor alike inaccurate sensationalism, wilful ignorance, and timid inaction." ASHA recognized how silence, misinformation and "wilful ignorance" allowed sexual exploitation and STIs to thrive.

STAMP OUT SYPHILIS—ENEMY OF YOUTH!

"Three-fourths of all syphilis infections are acquired by young people between the ages of 16 and 30 years."

Youth

Syphilis

Isn't it fair to warn her?
SYPHILIS CAN BE STAMPED OUT!
Ask— The American Social Hygiene Association
(Space here for the name of your agency)
HOW YOU CAN HELP!
This cartoon by the 1937 Pulitzer prize-winner was published by the *New York Daily News* on Second National Social Hygiene Day. By permission of the *News* and the artist the Association reproduces it as a poster. (See other side.)

Three principle goals of ASHA's early decades were sex education, eradicating prostitution and trafficking, and prevention and treatment of STIs. This essay focuses on these goals and briefly discusses examples of the ASHA programs that exemplify them. ASHA's first year of work included activity in all of these areas. The minutes for 1914 mention a wide range of activities that set the model for subsequent years. These included: community investigations; field visits; STI prevalence studies and other research; exhibits and publications; legislative work, including injunction and abatement laws that were used to close brothels; advocating the appointment of women police officers to oversee dance halls and other public spaces; working with the U.S. Bureau of Education to institute sex education in schools; university lecture appointments; correspondence with numerous organizations in Europe, South America, and Asia; and meetings with educators, school officials, professional organizations, social service organizations, and community groups in the United States. By 1916, ASHA estimated that its lecturers had reached 15,000 people and its exhibits had been viewed by 100,000. Subscriptions to its publications reached 30,000 and over 350,000 publications had been distributed. In addition, ASHA staff visited 127 cities and corresponded with 8,000 people.

PROMOTING SEX EDUCATION

Sex education was a core mission of ASHA and its predecessors. In May 1910, Delcevare King, a wealthy member of the Anti-Saloon League and social hygiene movement supporter, wrote to Prince Morrow proposing a "National Movement for Sex Education." His letter states that "The 'conspiracy of silence' on Sex is the most terrible failure of our civilization." King promised help raising funds for a national organization that eventually became the American Federation for Sex Hygiene and, later, ASHA. ASHA advocated sex education for young people and the general public, combating public silence about sexual health with educational programs. Its earliest sex education campaigns include information on basic reproduction that was factual for the time, but limited in scope. ASHA also promoted personal responsibility for sexual health and advocated sexual abstinence and moral purity believing this would lead to a healthy married life.

ASHA produced sex education pamphlets, exhibits, and poster displays for students, parents, medical professionals, youth-serving organizations, civic and industry groups, and educators. It also conducted studies on attitudes towards sex education. One of ASHA's core ideas in the early years was that the family was the basic social unit. It educated parents on how to talk to children about sexual health topics and advocated for sex education as a responsibility of both parents and schools. ASHA also contributed content for school and college-level sex education curricula and wrote guides on how to teach sex education for teachers and college students studying to be teachers.

Archival records demonstrate that ASHA was not just talking to its "inner circle" with these efforts. The annual reports for the 1910s and 1920s record lecture attendance and literature distribution totaling in the hundreds of thousands. By 1924, an estimated 750,000 college students had attended an ASHA lecture. Exhibits were viewed by tens of thousands annually, and the 1915 annual report stated that ASHA's gold-medal-winning exhibit at the Panama Pacific Exhibition was viewed by 100,000 people. The 1924 annual report also noted that ASHA's new exhibit would be installed in the "Hall of Health" at the Smithsonian Institution.

ASHA also used the relatively new mediums of radio and "motion pictures" to spread its educational message. The first sex education radio program aired on November 21, 1924 when ASHA-affiliated sex educator Bertha Chapman Cady spoke on the "Story of Life." ASHA produced documentary and feature-length dramatic films to spread its message as well. Annual reports from the 1920s show that ASHA films were loaned to state health departments and various professional conferences. Nearly 150 copies of ASHA films were sold in 1919-1920 and there were over 200 showings of its films in the same year. In 1933, ASHA collaborated with the Canadian Social Hygiene Council and Weldon Picture Corporation to produce *Damaged Lives*, a full-length feature film about a young man who contracts an STI as a result of an affair and infects his fiancée. The film, which reflects many of ASHA's sexual health messages, was shown in the United States, Canada and England to a positive response from viewers.

Another example of ASHA's early educational work is the *Keeping Fit* and *Youth and Life* sex education poster exhibits. These were designed for young men and women in 1920 and 1921 in collaboration with the United States Public Health Service. The posters contained basic information on reproduction and healthy lifestyles, as well as moral messages about responsibility, marriage, parenthood, and self-control. These early sex education tools would probably now be categorized as "abstinence education" and promoted traditional gender roles, but for their time they were remarkably frank and factual.

ERADICATION OF PROSTITUTION AND HUMAN TRAFFICKING

A second key part of ASHA's program was ending prostitution and trafficking. It fought against tolerance of prostitution in red light districts and promoted an "American Plan" of using legal, educational, and community activism as well as economic measures to try to wipe out prostitution. This method was viewed as a counter to the "European Plan" of tolerance and medical inspection.

ASHA wrote pamphlets and model laws documenting how to fight prostitution both on a national and local level. It conducted studies, issued reports, and created public relations materials on the economic, logistical and legal aspects of prostitution and to explain its role in disease transmission. ASHA also worked with international efforts to end human trafficking and prostitution through international studies, the League of Nations' anti-trafficking and anti-prostitution commissions, and efforts to pass international trafficking treaties. Its work in these areas demonstrated an understanding of trafficking and prostitution as an economic issue as well as a legal and public health problem.

A History and A Forecast, a pamphlet published in 1920, is a good example of how ASHA questioned the view that prostitution was a necessary evil and demonstrates ASHA's arguments against prostitution. The author contended that apologists for prostitution mimicked old pro-slavery rationalizations that some were meant to be enslaved, that slavery was an economic necessity and ending it would destroy property values, and that those who questioned the status quo were impractical visionaries. ASHA rejected these ideas when applied to prostitution and argued that "this supposedly fundamental social institution was a most artificial product. It existed solely by virtue of political corruption, stimulation of trade through advertising, and a white slave traffic to supply the artificially created demand."

STI PREVENTION AND TREATMENT

Understanding the medical context of ASHA's founding and early history helps to explain some of the organization's priorities and programs. Identification of the syphilis spirochete in 1905 and development of the Wasserman test for syphilis in 1906 allowed better diagnosis and better understanding of rates of infection and the epidemiology of STIs. The development of salvarsan in 1909 and neosalvarsan in 1914 offered new treatment options that improved on ages-old mercury treatment. However, treatment with these arsphenamine compounds was time-consuming, arduous, and potentially toxic to the patient. The public often resorted to "quack" or home remedies or simply remained ignorant of the cause and possible treatment of their symptoms.[2]

It was also difficult to track and prevent the spread of STIs due to public misconceptions as well as practices within the medical profession. Numerous records in the ASHA archives discuss how misunderstandings about STIs and the social stigma surrounding them made diagnosis difficult, especially when patients did not seek treatment or took home remedies and then spread the disease under the false impression that they were cured. They also include drastic, though sometimes contested, statistics on high rates of infection in the general population, fears

YOUTH AND LIFE

No. 1

AN EXHIBIT FOR GIRLS AND YOUNG WOMEN

APPROVED BY
THE UNITED STATES PUBLIC HEALTH SERVICE

PUBLISHED BY
THE AMERICAN SOCIAL HYGIENE ASSOCIATION
370 SEVENTH AVENUE, NEW YORK CITY

Why let it burn?

about "syphilis of the innocent" (meaning the wives and children of the infected individual), and eugenic ideas about STIs as a threat to "racial health" that added to a crisis atmosphere.

At the time of ASHA's founding, the medical profession was grappling with the competing needs of disclosing that a patient was infected to protect public health and the tradition of secrecy that had led most doctors up to that point to protect the privacy of infected individuals at the expense of their partners' health. ASHA promoted the importance of disclosure to the medical profession, but recognized that it was fighting a long-standing code of practice as well as the social stigma of STIs.

Many early publications by ASHA and its predecessors question the attitude of secrecy and lack of medical intervention for STIs when other infectious diseases were attacked so vigorously in late 19th early 20th centuries. In his summary of the hygiene movement, "Progress, 1900-1915," William Freeman Snow stated "...the public will soon assume the same attitude toward venereal infections that it does toward other dangerous communicable diseases. This attitude as expressed in tuberculosis or typhoid fever, for example, is one of sympathy and assistance for the infected indi-

vidual, while a frank and searching inquiry is made into the source of the infection and the conditions of the community which may have contributed to the opportunity for his infection." This "searching inquiry" was a key part of ASHA's work to prevent STIs.

Research projects included undercover investigations that identified "quack" healers and pharmacies that prescribed illegal, ineffective treatments. ASHA also promoted medical research in the testing and treatment of STIs, conducted research projects into STI infection rates and epidemiology, and did studies of hospital and clinic operations. It shared its findings broadly, including with governmental, medical, and private sector organizations, to promote treatment and prevent transmission. It also worked with professional associations, such as the American Medical Association and American Public Health Association, to get STIs on their agendas as a public health issue.

Reports and other documents in the archives show how ASHA staff attended medical conferences, corresponded with physicians, promoted updated knowledge about treatment protocols, disseminated methods of diagnosing and tracking STIs, published operational standards for clinics, and helped teach courses on STIs at medical schools. It also published the *Journal of So-*

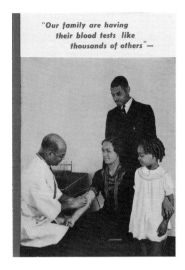

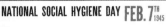

cial Hygiene, which was aimed at both a professional and lay audience, and distributed monthly updates to state venereal disease officers on diagnosis, treatment, social service follow up with patients, and recent research.

Examples of ASHA's large-scale prevention and treatment work can be seen in Social Hygiene Day and its programs during World War I and World War II. Social Hygiene Day, which started in 1937, was an annual series of public events, national media campaigns, and community action projects designed to promote ASHA's programs and drum up support for its work. Each year, ASHA selected a theme and developed a series of materials aimed at encouraging local individuals and groups to sponsor events and publicity efforts. Instructional kits for local Social Hygiene Day events show a wide range of activities including radio programs, exhibits on treatment and other related topics, conferences, poster contests, and newspaper stories. The public attention around Social Hygiene Day showed how much progress had been made from the days when sexual health topics could not be discussed in polite society and showed how far ASHA's work had helped to take the issue of sexual health.

World War I programs helped to set a model for work done during the following decades and cemented ASHA's relationship with the government, in particular the United States Public Health Service. STIs were a significant problem in the military during the war and high rates of STIs discovered in incoming military personnel added urgency to the entire ASHA program. ASHA staff were commissioned as army or navy officers or as part of the Commission on Training Camp Activities and collaborated with the United States Public Health Service.

ASHA worked with the U.S. War Department on two primary strategies. The first was to educate soldiers and civilian industrial workers about STIs and their transmission. The second strategy was to investigate and eliminate prostitution, which was recognized as the primary vehicle for STI transmission among the armed forces. ASHA was successful in shutting down many of the prostitution rings that traditionally surrounded military bases.

Educational programs for soldiers included pamphlets, health lectures, lantern slide shows, poster displays, and films. These employed themes of patriotism, comradeship and duty as well as factual information and moral persuasion to teach soldiers to remain disease-free and "fit to fight."

During World War II, ASHA fulfilled a role reminiscent of its work in World War I. ASHA had its hands full with the wartime military and industrial expansion and the resulting increase in prostitution and "sex delinquency." "Khaki-struck girls," wartime sexual freedoms, and single women moving to military and industrial zones to work for the war effort added a new element to ASHA's STI-prevention programs.

The 1943 annual report include Army estimates which suggested that as much as 70 percent of S T I s could be "traced to girls and women who were promiscuous or delinquent, though not prostitutes." It proposed the return of "social protection" activities, such as women police, control of venues serving alcohol, and supervised recreational activities or teen clubs. A S H A also proposed a school curriculum on "personal living in wartime" that acknowledged the likelihood of wartime relationships, but urged responsibility and abstinence as both a personal and patriotic responsibility.

The A S H A records include many World War II-era educational materials, such as sexual health training kits for officers, pamphlets for soldiers, and numerous fliers and posters. These show that education programs for soldiers used messages of patriotism and shared duty reminiscent of World War I. In addition, campaigns such as "Men Who Know Say No" warned soldiers not to trust appearances and abstain from casual relationships with pros t i tutes or "pick-ups." Cartoon poster series such as "Private Caution" and "Them Days is Gone Forever" used humor and peer pressure to suggest that soldiers who got infected with an S T I were "dopes" who had been fooled by a "good time girl." However, A S H A also acknowledged sexual activity and promoted condom use ("prophylaxis") and medical treatment at "pro stations" for those who did not "say no."

After decades of promoting research to improve the treatment of S T I s, A S H A was one of the many partners that helped to usher in the era of antibiotics. For example, A S H A staff served on the National Research Council Subcommittee on Venereal Diseases. The Council supervised numerous research projects, including experiments using penicillin to treat syphilis and gonorrhea. A S H A reports from 1944 discuss penicillin stating that it was "one of the greatest advances in therapy in the long history of medicine" and calling the new drug "a powerful weapon." True to form, A S H A reminded its constituents that there was still a lot of work to do to educate the public and medical community and to ensure effective treatment: "Even penicillin will not win our battle unless it is made

generally available and actually applied to infected persons." In short, "new and improved methods of treatment should not lull us into complacency but … stir us into still more intensified action." Though the development of penicillin was a pivotal event for A S H A, the organization continued to promote sexual health education, prevention, and treatment of S T I s, and work toward ending prostitution.

MOVING TOWARD SEXUAL HEALTH

Much has changed in the past 100 years in terms of medical knowledge, attitudes toward sexuality, and the tools available to promote sexual health. A S H A's archival records include perspectives about sex, gender roles, patient rights, public health, and a host of other issues that are diametrically opposed to what the organization believes today, yet A S H A's early work remains important. At a time when sexual topics were often repressed, A S H A advocated accurate sex education and proper treatment of S T I s. Although society usually tolerated sexual exploitation as long as it was invisible, A S H A fought the established attitude that prostitution was a necessary evil. The organization used research, community action, and education to bring these issues to light and break down the wall of silence surrounding them.

This essay has touched only briefly on examples of the many A S H A programs from 1914 through the 1940s. Many more are documented in the A S H A records, as are continuing and new activities in the 1950s through the early 2000s. In spite of the many changes in A S H A's outlook and priorities over time, the records show that A S H A consistently advocated for the availability of accurate sexual health information, free discussion of sexual health, and a collaborative responsibility for personal and public health as part of its mission of "Creating a Sexually Healthy Nation."

1 Allan Brandt, *No Magic Bullet: a Social History of Venereal Disease in the United States since 1880*, (New York: Oxford University Press, 1985), 46.
2 Ibid.

Pop Culture: Ignore it . . . if you have no FOMO[1] DEBORAH ARRINDELL

DEBORAH ARRINDELL is the vice president of health policy at the American Sexual Health Association. Ms. Arrindell has more than 30 years of experience in social and health policy, including work for women's economic justice, reproductive and sexual health, and employment and training.

I'M NOT TAKING LITERARY LICENSE when I say I had conversations with my son (late twenties) and my mom (late seventies) in the same month about *Fifty Shades of Grey*. And while it's extremely rare for African-American young men and their grandmothers (or any young men and their grandmothers) to be talking about the same books, it speaks volumes about the impact of that volume. It captured our national attention. With its low-lit prose and off-base depiction of BDSM, it started a public conversation about sex and pleasure. Why does it matter? Because this trilogy and the movie(s) that are being made from it have far greater reach than the scientifically accurate, consumer-friendly, award-winning publications that organizations and federal agencies create. The very fact that it's "popular" makes this aspect of our culture—the books, movies, slogans, television shows, and music that are being talked about now and shape our view of the world—difficult to track and follow. It's far reaching and wow, does it change fast. But we ignore the impact and potential of popular culture at our peril.

This is a lesson the White House has taken to heart. President Obama didn't go on *Late Night with Jimmy Fallon* to "slow jam the news" because he thought it would be fun (though clearly it was). It was part of a strategy to reach broad audiences. He also invited the media glitterati to the White House and asked for help in promoting the Affordable Care Act. His very funny "interview" with Zach Galifianakis on Funny or Die's *Between Two Ferns* was viewed by thousands and credited with a big bump in traffic on the government health care website. When questioned about whether it was "presidential" he replied, ". . . you want to remind yourself of the wonderful people that you are supposed to be serving who have a sense of humor and aren't thinking every day about position papers."

Hmmm. Doesn't everybody think every day about position papers? Maybe journal articles?

Fans of Lady Violet, the Dowager Countess on the nighttime soap opera *Downton Abbey*, watched in horror as her youngest granddaughter died in childbirth. When Lady Sybil struggled and sweated and died a painful death from eclampsia, who knew it would be a catalyst for discussions about maternal health? The American Public Health Association and other maternal health organizations moved quickly to offer more information via social media. Remember, they joined, rather than started, the conversation.

On an episode of *Grey's Anatomy*, the fictional Dr. Izzy Stevens explained to an HIV-infected patient that with appropriate medical care and treatment, there was a 98 percent chance that her baby would be healthy. "A 98 percent chance," the patient repeats. "A 98 percent chance," the doctor repeats. The Kaiser Family Foundation was the architect of that brief conversation. It was emotional and connected viewers with an important piece of information. A study after it aired showed it worked to provide viewers with facts they did not have. Oddly, as a nation we care what TV "doctors" say.

We also seem to care what our pop culture icons say when they're not in character. We applauded Angelina's (supposedly true pop culture icons can be identified by just one name) bold decision to talk about her preventive double mastectomy in an op-ed in the *New York Times*. We smiled when Michelle Obama took sweet potato fries and eggplant pizza to Jay Leno. We cringed when Michael Douglas bumbled through his throat cancer diagnosis. And we were touched when celebrities' moms—not to be confused with celebrity moms—took to the airways to tell us how wonderful their offspring were and the importance of health care. The moms of Jonah Hill, Alicia Keys, Adam Levine, and Jennifer Lopez urged young adults to get health care. Moms put up with a lot, but there's nothing worse than feeling their child isn't protected. Cleverly, the health care message doesn't come in until the second half of the two minute spot. Michelle Obama rounds out the piece with info about the Affordable Care Act. But by then, you're hooked. If not at hello, they certainly had me when Jonah flooded the elementary school.

Think about it this way. Pretty much everyone has heard of six degrees of Kevin Bacon. Pretty much no one has heard of six degrees of whoever the Surgeon General may be. Not only could most people not connect the Surgeon General to Kevin Bacon, they couldn't name the current Surgeon General.

Of course, popular culture and media icons often get it wrong. That's what happens when you don't read the scientifically accurate position paper.

In the third episode of the edgy show *Girls*, a character tests positive for HPV. The episode includes a broad array of misinformation, confusing information, and some stuff that's just plain wrong. Really wrong. But it's great that the show took a stab at it, because what followed were articles everywhere from the *New York Times* to popular blogs, writing about the show and correcting the misinformation. Hopefully, the accuracy lesson was learned. Importantly, it gave lots of folks an incentive to read more and learn more.

In all of these instances, health information is driven by popular culture. If it's clever, amusing, and engaging it's tweeted and retweeted, plastered on Facebook, and enters the blogosphere (I love that word). Then it becomes difficult for traditional news media outlets to ignore. It spreads and spreads.

Increasingly, there are efforts to better understand the intersection of health and culture. For many years, Hollywood, Health & Society at the University of Southern California Annenberg Norman Lear Center has provided assistance to entertainment industry professionals on story lines about health. More recently, a clever blog, Pop Health, curates and comments on the intersection of public health and pop culture.

It can be hard to keep up. Culture is ubiquitous, fluid, frenetic, huge. Constantly changing. Urgent and essential. I confess to doing a lousy job of keeping up. I feel a little like the "mature" woman in an ad who says she's going to stop making photo albums and start posting things to her wall: screen shot of all of her photos taped to her living room wall. Some days I feel like my nose is pressed against the social media, pop culture, high-tech window while it all whizzes by.

But I really do understand its importance. A former *Washington Post* ad slogan stated, "if you don't get it, you don't get it." IMHO[2] that's a critical first step, despite the challenges. I would embrace it fully if it didn't move so fast. So Laters, baby.[3]

1 Fear of Missing Out. Of course, it's likely no one uses this expression anymore. It's already feeling so 15 minutes ago.

2 In my humble opinion. Since it's used in all caps here it loses its humble quality.

3 Laters, baby. Farewell used by Christian Grey and available on t-shirts, key chains, magnets, jewelry, posters, and more. The expression actually has its own website.

What I Didn't Know LYNN BARCLAY

LYNN BARCLAY is the president of the American Sexual Health Association.

I want to thank all of the authors who wrote essays for this book. These are busy people who care as much about the subject of sexual health as we do. This project was a joy and could have been much larger since so many people were willing to share essays. You all have our most sincere thanks for your contributions to this book, but more importantly for all that you do to advance sexual health!

AS A PRODUCT OF A CATHOLIC SCHOOL IN THE 1970S, I arrived at college having had no sex education at all. Nothing. Nada. When I met the man who is now my husband of 34 years and we began to have fun dating and getting to know one another, I knew enough to go to the college health clinic for birth control. But clearly that's where my knowledge ended, because when I asked the doctor a question (I honestly don't remember the question), he made a face and asked how it was possible that I knew absolutely nothing. Needless to say I was totally embarrassed and didn't ask another thing. I remained totally uniformed to the point where I didn't know what I didn't know.

The summer I got engaged, I was having belly pains. No one could figure it out. I went to a few doctors until one told me something I didn't understand and added that I might never be able to get pregnant. What was this guy talking about? What did that have to do with belly pains? I was absolutely convinced he was a total quack. Again, I didn't know what I didn't know.

Early in our marriage my husband and I had a wonderful time building our lives together. We waited five or so years to start our family, but then we were ready. When it didn't happen, we went for help. I was told I had blocked tubes. No one ever explained to me how this might have happened. I remember my mother being confused as well. She told me that no one in the family had had that problem.

Finally we concluded that a birth child was not in our future and we adopted two amazing children, Miranda and Stephen. They are the absolute loves of our lives. I can't imagine loving two humans more than I love them, and feel unbelievably fortunate to have won the lottery with those two.

I started working at ASHA in 2005. This time I knew, or at least worried about, what I didn't know. How was a Catholic school girl who never learned a thing about STIs going to manage this important organization?

I learned amazing amounts of information during that first year, about sexually transmitted infections, how to talk to your doctor and partners, how to be in a healthy relationship, and so much more about the complicated and beautiful subject of sexual health. After about a year it hit me. I can remember the day. I suddenly flashed back to the belly pain I'd had that summer and realized I'd probably had a case of untreated chlamydia, which had caused pelvic inflammatory disease. And that is the reason my tubes were blocked. I finally knew what I hadn't known. Thank you ASHA.

ABOVE: *LYNN, MIRANDA, AND AVA*

My goal since I've been at ASHA is to make sure that no one else grows up without basic information like I did. Everyone should know—long before they get into sexual relationships—how to be sexually healthy and ASHA is going to continue to be a leader in helping people get all of the information they need.

ASHA has made enormous strides in the last century helping to educate people about STIs and give them the tools to protect themselves. I believe, however, that a message of sexual health, is far more empowering. And I believe that by adopting this message, this one-hundred-year-old nonprofit can continue making an important difference in the lives of Americans of all ages.

This picture is of me, my daughter Miranda, and her daughter Ava. Miranda knows far more about sexual health than I did at her age and I believe she will make sure that Ava knows as much if not more than she does. That's the key isn't it? Raising the next generations to be sexually healthy.

17

A Century of Hypocrisy: America's Ever Conflicted Views on Sexual Health and Sexuality TOM BEALL

TOM BEALL is the Chair of the Board of Directors of the American Sexual Health Association. For nearly three decades, as Managing Director of the Health and Social Marketing Practices at Ogilvy Public Relations, Tom has been at the forefront of applying health communications to addressing many of America's leading public health issues.

IT ONLY TOOK THE AMERICAN SEXUAL HEALTH ASSOCIATION (ASHA) 100 years to find the will to put the term "sexual health" in its name. At its outset in 1914, in keeping with the times, ASHA was the American Social Hygiene Association. In 1960, it was bold enough to become the American Social Health Association, replacing a focus on hygiene with a focus on health. Only in 2013 did sexual health emerge from ASHA's proverbial closet. Is there any doubt that there are challenges, real and perceived, associated with talking explicitly and positively about sexual health in America if an organization created to focus on it took nearly a century to embrace the term in its own name?

The irony: over those same 100 years, we have become a hyper-sexualized nation. Sex, sexuality, and sexual tension are part of our lives 24/7. Sexual content and imagery fill our books, magazines, movies, and television programs. Take a look at TV alone, our most widely-shared avenue of communication. From *Days of Our Lives* to *Masters of Sex* to *Sex Sent Me to the ER*, TV in all of its forms— soaps, daytime talk shows, prime time dramas, sitcoms, reality shows, news, documentaries, and advertising—provides overwhelming evidence that we are focused on all things sexual.

Unfortunately, our approach to sexual health itself is often characterized by hypocrisy. While popular culture blares sexual imagery, silence, stigma, and shame all too often surround our personal and collective consideration of sexual health. Most of us can't even find the words to talk positively and constructively about it with our children, our healthcare providers, and even our partners. We respond with outrage and disgust to sex scandals and turn private sexual relationships into public controversies. We show ambivalence in our approaches to educating our youth and accepting the sexuality of our elders.

Our cultural hypocrisy prompted Walter Russell Mead to observe in "America's Addled Puritanism," an essay published on November 11, 2012 in *The American Interest*, "We are simultaneously the most licentious and sexually open society since Nero was fiddling around in Rome, and the most uptight and rigid country this side of Saudi Arabia. Our social judgments and tolerance about sexual behavior swing back and forth between the views of the Marquis de Sade and those of Cotton Mather depending on complex and ever-changing calculations."

WE HAVE COME A LONG WAY

ASHA's history of navigating the often troubling waters of sexual health mirrors the distance that American culture has travelled since 1914. Throughout the intervening century, ASHA has both reflected and influenced change in societal progress, norms, and expectations. A few notable examples:

- In the 1910s, distribution of contraception is illegal and the nation's first birth control clinic opens in Brooklyn, only to be shut down days later by the city's vice squad. American men go to war, and American women march to secure their voting rights. Meanwhile, ASHA is formed by Thomas Hepburn, MD and Charles Eliot, among other social hygienists who thought that teaching people about "proper uses of sexuality" would help stamp out venereal disease and the sexual double standard that kept women from achieving full equality. ASHA also is commissioned to produce posters with non-moralistic messages explaining that winning the war requires disease-free solders.

- In the 1940s, men (and women) are again going to war, and ASHA once again becomes involved in VD education campaigns among the armed forces. Women are entering the workforce in growing numbers and beginning to enjoy what comes to be recognized in time as their "liberation." ASHA meanwhile is ahead of the curve, having begun to sponsor nationwide observances of social hygiene days aimed at encouraging and supporting community and family discussions of sexual health.

- In the 1960s, the Pill is approved and the sexual revolution begins to unfold . . . well, explode. Gay pride parades are launched and bras are burned. ASHA finds the courage to change its name to the American Social Health Association. In announcing the name change, ASHA Executive Director Conrad Van Hyning observes "the shift from hygiene to health emphasizes that we are keeping up with the times. ASHA has always been a pioneering national agency working in new, and sometimes not popular nor well understood causes."

- In the 1970s and 1980s, America enthusiastically embraces the "joys of sex," while waking up to the risks that can be associated with sexual activity. Rising STI rates and new public awareness prompt ASHA to launch the first modern STI-prevention awareness campaign, and with CDC support, ASHA operates a toll-free information and referral service that soon was taking more than 100,000 calls per year. Then, as AIDS begins to extract its tragic toll, ASHA is awarded the CDC contract to establish the National AIDS Hotline and for 18 years, ASHA helped America respond to AIDS by talking one-on-one to many millions of callers (at its peak the hotline answered more than one million calls per year).

BUT WE HAVE A LONG WAY TO GO

Fast-forward to the 21st century. Sex and sexuality have entered the digital age. More and more of our sexual health education occurs online and in pop culture, including online dating, cybersex, and sexting. More and more of us, especially our youth and young adults, are turning to Google, Bing, and YouTube to learn the facts of life. We look to shows like *The Bachelor*, *The Bachelorette*, *16 and Pregnant*, and *Teen Mom* to learn about how to handle love, relationships, and, yes, sex.

In this dynamic, sexually charged environment, ASHA has renewed its commitment to help create a sexually healthy nation. What does this mean for individuals and our broader society? ASHA believes that sexual health is the ability to embrace and enjoy our sexuality throughout our lives. It is an important part of our physical and emotional health. Being sexually healthy means:

- Understanding that sexuality is a natural part of life and involves more than sexual behavior.

- Recognizing and respecting the sexual rights we all share.

- Having access to sexual health information, education, and care.

- Making an effort to prevent unintended

pregnancies and STIs and seek care and treatment when needed.

- Being able to experience sexual pleasure, satisfaction, and intimacy when desired.

- Being able to communicate about sexual health with others including sexual partners and healthcare providers.

But while ASHA will continue to promote sexual health as an essential part of overall health and work toward the goal of creating a sexually healthy nation, let's not underestimate the weight of history and the challenges that we must overcome. For example:

- Comprehensive school-based sexual health education has become captive to the political divides that define contemporary America, as charted in Laurie Abraham's November 20, 2011 cover story for *The New York Times Magazine*, "Teaching Good Sex." Abraham defines comprehensive sex education as "nonjudgmental instructions on bodies, birth control, disease prevention and 'healthy relationships'—all geared to helping teenagers make responsible choices, one of which might be choosing to become sexually intimate with someone." She observes that "by the end of the 1980s, sex ed had taken its place in the basket of wedge issues dividing the right and left." The price to be paid: a generation lacking the knowledge and ability to navigate the sometimes challenging landscape of sexuality and sexual health.

- Our courts and legislatures also have a chilling effect on making America sexually healthy. Despite recent forward-looking and encouraging decisions regarding marriage equality and gay and lesbian rights, our courts and legislatures are "squeamish" about sex. In her November 24, 2013 op-ed in *The Washington Post,* "Most People Like Sex. Why Don't Judges," law professor Margo Kaplan demonstrates how courts and state legislatures choose to ignore if not deny the joy of sex. Sexual pleasure, she observes, tends to be treated "as a topic to be avoided or an immoral indulgence the state should

prevent. When they address sex, they often reveal their embarrassment by using Victorian-sounding euphemisms such as 'an intimate relation of husband and wife' or awkwardly clinical terms such as 'the physical act.' Other times, they express outright disgust." Squeamish courts, Kaplan concludes, lead to bad laws.

- Antiquated obscenity laws and long-embedded fear of offense also exert strong influence on how some media channels restrict medically responsible discussions of sexual health. In her *Washington Post* op-ed, Kaplan also noted that our outdated approach to obscenity laws allows states to "freely ban all material that depicts sexual activity 'in a patently offensive way' and 'appeals to the prurient interests.'" First Amendment protections, she adds, "kick in only if the material has other serious value—literary, artistic, political or scientific—to redeem it." However, like beauty, the definitions of offensive and prurient interests lie in the eye of the beholder. Such antiquated laws fuel the restrictive policies of many media outlets that place unwarranted limits on responsible public discussion of sexual health. Examples include restrictions on bloggers responsibly discussing sexual topics, ad bans that equate responsible sexual health tips with pornography and lewd or provocative images, email filters that automatically send messages with the words "sexual health" into spam files, and mobile marketing practices that filter out specific words like "breast" or "condom" from text messages.

For 100 years, ASHA has faced challenges such as these head on and worked to create a sexually healthy nation by educating the public and raising awareness about preventing STIs, advocating for sound, science-based sexual health policy, and openly—and honestly—communicating about sex and sexuality. Now we are intent to redouble our efforts, turning sexual health from a taboo topic to one that is talked about and supported far, wide, and responsibly.

The Family Planning Safety Net:
Time-Tested and Trusted CLARE COLEMAN

CLARE COLEMAN is the
president and CEO of the National
Family Planning & Reproductive
Health Association (NFPRHA),
a membership organization for
family planning administrators
and clinicians serving the nation's
low-income and uninsured.
Coleman previously served as
CEO of Planned Parenthood
Mid-Hudson Valley (NY), and
spent 12 years on Capitol Hill,
most recently as chief of staff f
or U.S. Representative Nita Lowey
(D-NY).

ON JANUARY 8, 1964, PRESIDENT LYNDON JOHNSON declared war on an enemy that was difficult to define: poverty. "Our aim," Johnson said, "is not only to relieve the symptom of poverty, but to cure it and, above all, to prevent it." With these words, he launched an effort that, 50 years in, has changed the quality of life for millions of Americans in ways that many today take for granted, including expanded access to education and public health services, improvements in the environment, and progress toward creating a more equal society.

The War on Poverty was also a turning point for reproductive rights, a marker from which we can measure our successes as well as the progress yet to be made. Within a decade of Johnson's declaration, Medicaid, the health insurance program for the poorest Americans, was well established, with family planning services included as a mandatory benefit, which is evidence of the enduring economic benefits of planning pregnancies and spacing births. The United States Supreme Court recognized the right to privacy in reproductive decision-making and affirmed the legal right of women to choose when, or even whether, they would have children, in the landmark rulings of *Griswold v. Connecticut* (1965), *Eisenstadt v. Baird* (1972), and *Roe v. Wade* (1973). And in 1970, Title X of the Public Health Service Act, the nation's first and only federal family planning program, was created—with then–United States Congressman George H.W. Bush as its chief sponsor. At the time, Bush said, "We need to make population and family planning household words. We need to take sensationalism out of this topic…. If family planning is anything, it is a public health matter." The law creating Title X passed the House 298–32; the Senate vote was unanimous.

Publicly funded family planning has provided essential health care to tens of millions of low-income, uninsured, and underinsured women and men over the ensuing decades, and it remains the cornerstone of sexual and reproductive health care delivery today. With the help of these health centers, generations of women (and men!) have been empowered to make decisions that enabled them to avoid unintended pregnancy and plan and space births, which, in turn, better enabled them to pursue higher education, enter the workforce, and lead healthier, happier lives.

We have seen tremendous progress on numerous fronts over the years in the march toward achieving full reproductive rights. The last three years alone

21

ABOVE: *CRISTIAN, AVA, AND MIRANDA*

have yielded significant advancements to the benefit of millions of women and men of reproductive age. After years of pushback against misleading and dishonest abstinence-only-until-marriage programs, evidence-based, comprehensive sexuality education was finally funded at the federal level. The Affordable Care Act (ACA) is increasing insurance coverage of and access to health care nationwide. Thanks to the women's preventive health services requirement included in the health care law, millions of women now have insurance coverage for their annual exams and their contraceptive methods and counseling, without co-pays. And millions more low-income women who were previously uninsured now have access to this care through Medicaid.

Yet despite our successes, access has yet to be fully realized. Millions are left out of the expansion of insurance coverage under the ACA, and many of

our neighbors remain one unanticipated event away from needing help from the safety net, which includes publicly funded health services, food stamps, and free school lunches. That safety net has been strained over the years by tough economic times; by the enduring challenges of poverty, mobility, and inequality in our society; and, increasingly, by political attack.

But there's reason for hope: as attacks on the safety net and on access to sexual and reproductive health services in particular have increased in intensity, we have also seen a renewed defense of those services and their dedicated providers. Americans have reacted by flocking to social media, organizing protests, and launching campaigns, which has in turn emboldened elected officials at both the federal and state levels to say "enough is enough." This new level of engagement gives us confidence that no effort to dismantle the safety net will be allowed to slip by unnoticed.

Working Toward Sexual Health Promotion   ELI COLEMAN, PhD

ELI COLEMAN, PhD, is the academic chair in sexual health, professor, and director of the Program in Human Sexuality, Department of Family Medicine and Community Health, at the University of Minnesota Medical School in Minneapolis. He is the author of numerous articles and books on sexual health, and the founding editor of both the *International Journal of Transgenderism* and the *International Journal of Sexual Health*.

IN THE PAST DECADE, THERE HAVE BEEN SIGNIFICANT CHANGES in the discourse of public health regarding sexual health. Recently, there has been a significant leap in the recognition of sexual health as a central component of overall health. But this has been a long journey over the last century. Our understanding of sexual health has moved slowly from a purely disease perspective to a broader perspective of what it means to be sexually healthy.

The most notable advance of the construct occurred when the World Health Organization (WHO) convened meetings and produced a technical document in 1975 which made the first attempt at defining sexual health. The definition read as follows:

Sexual health is the integration of the somatic, emotional, intellectual and social aspects of sexual being, in ways that are positively enriching and that enhance personality, communication and love.

In the next paragraph, the authors wrote, "Fundamental to this concept are the right to sexual information and the right to pleasure." The document went on to cite Mace, Bannerman, and Burton, who described sexual health as containing three basic elements: (1) the capacity to enjoy and control sexual and reproductive behavior in accordance with a social and personal ethic; (2) a freedom from fear, shame, guilt, false beliefs, and other psychological factors inhibiting sexual response and impairing sexual relationships; and (3) freedom from organic disorders, diseases, and deficiencies that interfere with sexual and reproductive functions. The WHO document concluded, "Thus the notion of sexual health implies a positive approach to human sexuality, and the purpose of sexual health care should be the enhancement of life and personal relationships and not merely counselling and care related to procreation or sexually transmitted diseases."

The emergence of the AIDS pandemic in the 1980s put pressure on health ministries to develop new approaches to sexual health promotion. The combined burden of the HIV/AIDS pandemic, increases in unintended pregnancies, greater awareness of sexual violence, and greater publicity about sexual dysfunctions and disorders highlighted the urgent need for enhanced sexuality education and a much more concerted approach to addressing sexuality problems. A new public health mandate began to emerge to address these sexual health issues in a comprehensive manner. At this juncture a significant step occurred where the term "sexual health" became incorporated into the discourse on a public health level.

As conversations continued, new definitions were developed. Most significant were the definitions that were created by the Pan American Health Organization/Regional Office of the World Health Organization (PAHO) and by the U.S. Surgeon General, both in 2000. Two years later, WHO embarked on a revision of its definition that was by then almost three decades old.

Probably the most controversial issue that has daunted the construction of these definitions is pleasure. The right to pleasure as essential to attainment of sexual health was acknowledged in the 1975 document, but not included in the definition itself, nor was it included in the PAHO definition. Interestingly, the concept of pleasure was included in the WHO 2002 working definition. In some ways it is a rather revolutionary concept that government policies and public health approaches should be designed not just to avoid problems of illness and infertility, but to promote pleasure as an essential ingredient of well-being.

To have sexual rights that included pleasure articulated by the WHO was a significant step in the history of public health, particularly because the rights imply individual and societal responsibility. That this step can be a difficult one within the public health world was certainly illustrated in the attempt by the Centers for Disease Control and Prevention (CDC) to develop its own definition in 2010. The definition constructed embodied many of the concepts in previous definitions but avoided the discussion of sexual rights and did not include the concept of pleasure.

In addition to these, the Trojan™ Sexual Health Advisory Council and more recently the American Sexual Health Association developed more consumer-friendly definitions that embodied the basic concepts, including rights and pleasure, but made them more accessible to the public.

The public health imperative of developing a strategic and comprehensive approach to sexual health promotion has been articulated over and over again in the last century. But recently something fundamen-

tal has shifted. A new era has begun. Sexual health has been recognized as a key strategy in promoting overall health and well-being. In 2008 alone, several international documents were produced which assert the centrality of sexual health in public health promotion at the highest levels of public health strategies. The responsibility of the state has been made clear: to respond strategically and comprehensively to the large number of sexual health issues.

In many of the sexual health documents, the recommendations for promoting sexual health are also highly consistent and include the following:

- Create better climates for discussion of sexuality;

- Increase access to information and education about sexuality;

- Develop prevention strategies to include community-based intervention;

- Enhance access to care for sexual concerns; and

- Increase research in human sexuality and evaluation of programs designed to promote sexual health.

As governments and public health experts struggle with the complexities of the sexual problems that face their nations, they will need to continue to develop strategies to promote sexual health and keep in mind that sexual health has been recognized as a basic human right for all.

Our Stories: The Impact of Religion on Sexual Health

LATESHA ELOPRE, MD, & NICHOLAS VAN WAGONER, MD, PhD

ORGANIZED RELIGION WIELDS GREAT POWER in the United States and across the globe, providing cultural and structural guidance that often defines relationships, creates social networks of like-minded individuals, and provides a lens through which human experience is interpreted. Relying on ancient religious texts, modern religious authority sometimes views sexuality and sexual behavior with suspicion, allocating moral weight (and spiritual condemnation) to different forms of sexuality and to specific sexual acts. Philosophies that see our corporal existence as a spiritual testing ground (with eternal consequences hanging in the balance) often look at sex for procreation favorably and condemn non-procreative behaviors as sin. In this model, genetically driven but religiously condemned behaviors such as masturbation and sex outside of marriage (either heterosexual or homosexual) may portend shame and secrecy for the "sinner," justify stigmatization, and allow for condemnation of the sinner, especially when sexually transmitted infections, including HIV, result.

The World Health Organization defines sexual health as a positive and respectful approach to sexuality and sexual relationships, describing sexual expression as pleasurable, safe experiences free of coercion, discrimination, and violence. Inherent in this concept of sexual health is the belief that sexual rights must be respected, protected, and fulfilled. The conflicts are obvious, the questions clear: Is sexual health achievable for members of a culture strongly influenced by religious philosophies that discriminate between acceptable and unacceptable sexuality and sexual behaviors, and that tend to label and condemn individuals who violate said strictures as sinners? Further, what are the

potential personal and public health consequences of discounting the impact of religious philosophy on an individual's sexual health?

In the following two personal essays, we share how religion influenced our perceptions of sexuality and sexual behavior.

LATESHA: Like many people, at a very young age my religion shaped my personal beliefs and actions by providing a moral compass. My first memory of being in church is clicking my black, patent leather shoes together to the beat of the choir. I was two years old and I remember feeling joy. I did not question scripture, my pastor, or my church. This type of blind faith has its merits by providing a security blanket that allows the wearer to feel self-assured and never alone.

Never questioning, my first beliefs about sexuality were focused on abstinence and the idea that homosexuality was a sin. Women who had children out of wedlock were shunned from the church and people who engaged in homosexual acts without repentance were doomed to spend their eternal afterlife in flames. My beliefs did not change for many years until I learned the truth about a family secret.

When I was eight years old, I watched a beloved uncle die a very slow and painful death from cancer. His death was the first time in my life I felt true sorrow. My sorrow deepened when at the age of thirteen I realized I had never really known him at all. I discovered that my uncle had been gay and actually died from AIDS. I began to question the love I had for him, for how can you truly love someone you do not know? How could he have died, never being able to be himself around the people he loved? My faith was tested and ques t i oning it caused me immense despair.

Growing up as an African-American female in my community, there was no gray for me when considering what was right and wrong in regards to sexuality. For years I struggled with my previous beliefs that homosexuality was disgusting and sinful. My belief that HIV was a punishment from God and the lack of empathy I'd had for those whose lives it claimed. I now feel shame for the person I once was and wonder if I ever shamed my uncle.

I cannot say that this is how Christianity shapes everyone's ideas of sexual health, but this is how it shaped mine. For a time I stepped away from the church searching for inner perspective and reflection. Today, I have let most of my anger go and try to help the people in my community who HIV is currently affecting the most. And while I may never have that same security blanket my faith previously provided, I find myself wanting it for my son. I would like for him to feel the joy and fellowship that I felt sitting in the pews, no matter what his sexual identity may be or who he chooses to love.

NICK: I was four years old when I first recognized my same-sex attraction. Growing up the fifth child of parents who were devout members of the Church of Jesus Christ of Latter-day Saints (Mormons), I quickly learned that such attractions were not only unwelcome but considered by God (and his earthly representatives) second only to murder in spiritual condemnation. By the age of 15, and despite possessing but a naïve understanding of sex, I'd accepted my fate—I would die from HIV, God's punishment for my same-sex attraction. Throughout adolescence and early adulthood, I was terrified that my family and friends and those within my religious circle would discover my same-sex sexual attraction, and I begged God to change me. But despite my incessant pleas, despite my commitment to service and abstinence from same-sex relationships of any type, change did not come.

At the age of 22, I publically acknowledged my sexual orientation. Shortly thereafter, my religious community

convened a court to formally punish me. I was offered a choice: change my same-sex attraction and remain a member of my faith or continue on my current trajectory and suffer the spiritual and social consequences— "disfellowshipment" from my church, or excommunication, the LDS equivalent of spiritual execution.

Having finally accepted my same-sex attraction and unwilling to attempt change, I was disfellowshipped from the LDS church. In that moment, I lost my religious social network and friends, and was condemned by the organization and God whom I had tried to serve all of my life. Fortunately, my family members remained (and remain) supportive and became my advocates and guardians helping me navigate this dark time.

Tempered by years, I am now able to reflect upon my religious upbringing with a good deal of fondness. I recognize its personal and societal value, while remaining keenly aware of its influence on my own sexual health, past and present. For those like me, who harbored (or still harbor) strong religious beliefs that clash with personal sexuality and/or sexual behavior, shame and guilt have levied their fee.

In many ways, we are both grateful for having had a religious upbringing—its positive personal (both spiritual and physical) and societal benefits are irrefutable. Yet to declare that religion is without unintentional, untoward consequences may be dangerous with respect to sexual health. While we believe that sexual health is an inherent human right, it will remain foreign and unachievable unless we acknowledge and challenge the control that some religions have over this realm.

LATESHA ELOPRE, MD, is a second year infectious diseases fellow at the University of Alabama at Birmingham (UAB). She is currently pursuing an MSPH in Applied Epidemiology at UAB's School of Public Health. She lives with her husband, a dedicated middle school art teacher, and son, Jacob.

NICHOLAS VAN WAGONER, MD, PhD, is an assistant professor in the Department of Medicine, Division of Infectious Diseases, University of Alabama at Birmingham. He currently lives in Birmingham with his partner of 17 years and his two Labrador retrievers, Emma and Alex.

Adolescent Sexual Health is Not an Oxymoron

J. DENNIS FORTENBERRY, MD, MS

J. DENNIS FORTENBERRY, MD, MS, is a sexual health researcher and adolescent medicine physician. He is professor of pediatrics at Indiana University School of Medicine.

ADULTS OF ANY AGE WERE ADOLESCENTS for almost a decade, *once upon a time*. The echoes of the sexual lives of those born in 1914 are becoming faint, but the successive generations of their children also traversed an adolescence marked by the initiations of sexual lives that still ring brightly. Infants born during 2014—ASHA's centennial year—will be 86 years of age at the turn of the 22nd century, with many still living in 2114. The coming century will witness hundreds of millions of sexual acts, each creating the cobweb threads of sexuality and sex linking the next century to the past. But how will we view their adolescent sexuality and that of those who come after?

In this last century there has been a persistent emphasis on virginity as a pertinent social status, and abstinence as a social and public health solution to sexually transmitted infections and early pregnancy. Anxiety about these issues was no less evident in the discourses around adolescent sexuality in 1914 than it is today. Now as then, this emphasis on virginity and abstinence creates an oxymoron out of the phrase "adolescent sexual health" because, according to many adults, almost no sexual behavior *chosen* by adolescents can simultaneously meet expectations for "sexual" and "health."

This choice becomes a huge challenge for many when adolescents engage in sexual behaviors other than abstinence—masturbation, kissing, and coitus, to name a few. The great failure of abstinence as a singular social and public health frame for adolescent sexual health is the celebration of one behavioral choice, and the suppression of others. The outcome is a recurrent insistence on pathologizing adolescent sexuality which runs through our social commentary, our public health policy, our school-based education, and our clinical care of adolescents.

Adolescents continue to be euphemistically defined as "sexually experienced" based on the occurrence (or not) of a single coital event. This terminology—still commonly used in clinical and public health settings—unfortunately coincides with social proscriptions of penile-vaginal intercourse as the one behavior that "counts" and religious prescriptions of virginity as a desired social status.

The emphasis on abstinence and virginity also play a key part in a larger public health principle I call "the sexual risk paradigm." The sexual risk paradigm has been a serviceable workhorse for decades of public health prevention efforts for adolescent pregnancy and sexually transmitted infections (STIs). It has taught us many lessons about the behavioral factors associated with excess

ABOVE & FOLLOWING PAGE: *CARLOS*

and differential risk of early pregnancy and STIs and it has led us to some success. Increasingly, however, the harsh lessons of the epidemics of sexual violence, STIs, and HIV have illuminated the limitations of this paradigm.

One important limitation is the lack of capacity for addressing the social and structural factors which are typically stronger than individual factors for the prediction of pregnancy or STI risk. Poverty, education, region of residence, gender, and access to care are examples of risk predictors acknowledged but not addressed by the sexual risk paradigm, despite the fact that they closely shape the contexts in which adolescents make their sexual choices.

A second important contradiction of the sexual risk paradigm is its contribution to the stigmatization of persons associated with behaviors designated as "sexual risks." Attribution of responsibility is an important element of the stigma associated with STI/

HIV, and the sexual risk paradigm suggests that persons with STI/HIV are irresponsibly unable to control their sexual behaviors. The sexual risk paradigm thus generates stigma when individual risks are supplanted by group-based risk stratification, creating "high risk" and "low risk" groups. Not surprisingly, the groups correspond to existing social stratifications made by age, race, socioeconomic status, and patterns of sexual partnering. Stigma and high risk/low safety behaviors are closely coupled, and the sexual risk paradigm inevitably reifies not just stigma but stereotypes as well.

I suggest a shift to an "adolescent sexual health paradigm" that can redress the limitations of our current thinking. "*Sexual health*" and "*healthy sex*" are related but dis t i nct terms that address the ways by which individual, interpersonal, and social benefits of sexuality are maximized while risks are minimized. *Sexual health* reflects an educational and public health philosophy that endorses the importance of sexuality in all lives. The term falls among those familiar topics that reflect quotidian experience but, from a scientific perspective, are difficult to pin to a reliably precise definition. Definitions of adolescent sexual health need to include four core issues of sexual rights, knowledge, choice, and pleasure. Focus on these core areas brings social and public health attention to the structural components of sexual risk. This focus also provides leverage against the sexual stigma often generated by the sexual risk paradigm.

The new paradigm will help reframe abstinence (and other sexual behaviors) as *chosen* by adolescents. Abstinence should not be seen as sexual void, often associated with both social and psychological suppression of sexuality. Rather, abstinence should reflect a self-conscious assessment of familial expectations, relationship commitments, sexual interests, and the ebb and flow of daily life. We know that adolescents have the developmental maturity and cognitive capacity to make these types of choices because, in fact, many generations have chosen to be abstinent through some or all of their adolescence. Hardly anyone would consider the *choice* of abstinence to be a bad thing.

At the same time, the new paradigm recognizes that adolescent sexual health is much more than attempts to prevent or delay coitus. It involves the understanding of sexual anatomy, awareness of gendered rules for sexual display and modesty, recognition of sexual desire in self and others, consciousness of sexual boundaries, and knowledge of the methods available for preventing STIs and pregnancy. Sexual learning includes a variety of sexual feelings and behaviors: sexual attractions, arousal, and pleasure accompany masturbation, kissing, fellatio, cunnilingus, and coitus. It also includes experience of the difficulties of sex—erectile dysfunction, pain, lubrication difficulty, lack of pleasure. Sexual learning, then, is a critical element of development with relevance to adolescent health as well as to various life course trajectories that summarize adult sexual health.

It would be nice to think that our contemporary understanding of adolescents' sexual health is simply an advanced point along some inevitable continuum leading to an ideal state of perfect sexual health. Certainly, the idea that sexual health is important in each person's life—perhaps especially each young person's life—has become more generally accepted in 2014 than it was in 1914. Yet, we are still struggling with engaging young people's sexuality in ways that bring them into healthy adulthood. From a public health perspective, we're still struggling to transform an outmoded sexual risk paradigm into a functional one that accepts and embraces adolescent sexual health.

HIV and the City:
Learning About the Epidemic ROBERT FULLILOVE, EdD

ROBERT FULLILOVE, EdD, is
the associate dean for community
and minority affairs, professor
of clinical sociomedical sciences
and the co-director of the Cities
Research Group at Columbia
University's Mailman School of
Public Health. He has authored
numerous articles in the area of
minority health and has served on
Institute of Medicine committees
that have produced reports on
a variety of topics including
substance abuse and addiction,
HIV/AIDS, tuberculosis, and
damp indoor spaces and health.

I BEGAN DOING HIV/AIDS RESEARCH IN 1986 at the University of California, San Francisco. Mindy Fullilove, the director of our fledgling research group, was convinced, then as she is now, that the intense focus of prevention researchers on the demographics of the epidemic was misguided. The fact that AIDS rates were disproportionately high among African Americans and Latinos led to the notion that the factors that distinguish members of one racial group from another—and here I refer to behavioral, attitudinal, and socioeconomic differences—must also hold the key to explaining why, as early as the mid-80s, the epidemic in non-white communities had a different character than it did in white communities.

While such differences clearly were present, Mindy strongly believed that we were not paying sufficient attention to the ways in which the *geography* of the epidemic had as much to do, if not more, with AIDS prevalence and incidence rates than differences in the behavioral and demographic characteristics of the individuals at risk. Differences in infection rates between urban and rural populations were not sufficiently examined, she insisted, and AIDS researchers were largely ignoring the heavy concentration of AIDS in poor communities of color that clearly involved significant interactions between individuals and their immediate environment.

Her interest was driven by more than just a need to develop regression models that explained ever increasing variations in HIV/AIDS rates. Locating the problem of HIV in individuals was also connected to the notion that what prevention researchers needed to do was find ways of fixing the person. If she was correct, then failing to identify the environmental factors that might be fixed to improve our chances of preventing HIV infection was a significant failure in our programmatic, policy, and research efforts.

In essence, she was concerned about the differences in working to change risky injection use behaviors among intravenous drug users versus working to eliminate shooting galleries—places where users can purchase drugs, share needles, and shoot up—as risk environments that contributed enormously to the epidemic that we were studying in New York City. Obviously, there were advantages to each of these approaches, but in the late 1980s and early 90s many of our colleagues were amused by our efforts. Still, this did little to sway the direction of much of the behavioral research that consumed the time and resources of so many prevention specialists.

As I fast-forward to the present day, I am hugely impressed by how far the field of HIV/AIDS research has come. The moment public health researchers in a variety of fields began to tease apart and parse the "social determinants of health," they also began to study a variety of factors in addition to race, ethnicity, and individual risk behavior profiles. Mindy still maintains a toe in HIV/AIDS research, but her major efforts have examined how urban development in the United States has created cities that are risk environments for a host of conditions that we lump under the rubric of health disparities.

I have continued to work with her analysis in my efforts to understand the ever-changing patterns of the HIV/AIDS epidemic. I have tried to demonstrate that the "War on Drugs" that began in the 1970s not only incarcerated significant numbers of people who had been exposed to HIV long before it was recognized in our midst in 1981, but the heavy concentration of police in poor neighborhoods of color has ensured that many people who were living with the virus would cycle in and out of our state and federal prisons. The U.S. system of mass incarceration has meant that the proportion of prisoners living with HIV would constantly be significantly higher than is the case in the general population.

Given the high rates of recidivism, individuals cycle into prison, out again and then back to prison again within three to five years. This pattern, I have insisted, has done incredible damage to our HIV-prevention efforts. The large numbers of men (and increasingly, of women) who are taken from these communities have completely altered the social dynamics of community life. What community, I have been led to ask, can suffer the loss of 50 percent of its adults and not be horrifically damaged in every aspect of community life from child rearing, to marriage and mating rituals, to managing family and community economic resources?

The epidemic has exploited the ecological niche that was created when these communities went into sharp decline. Improving of our efforts to fight HIV will require fixing our cities. Doing so will also have a dramatic impact on the general health of the entire community as well.

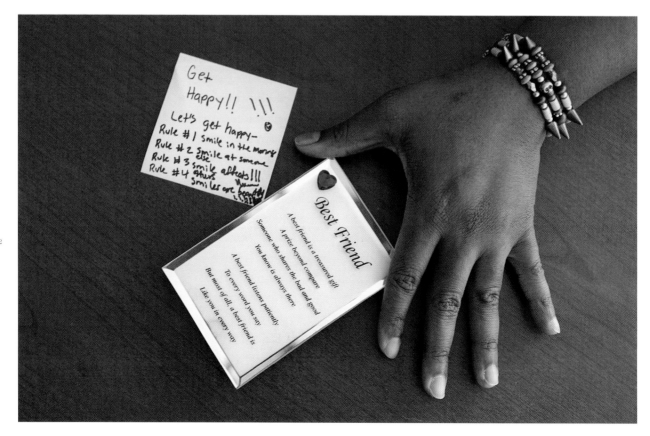

STDs at the End of ASHA's First Century

H. HUNTER HANDSFIELD, MD

H. HUNTER HANDSFIELD, MD, is Professor Emeritus of Medicine at the University of Washington Center for AIDS and STD, and former director of the Sexually Transmitted Diseases Control Program for Public Health—Seattle & King County, Washington. He has been at the forefront of STD research and prevention for four decades and is the 2010 recipient of the American STD Association's Distinguished Career Award. Dr. Handsfield recently completed six years as a member of ASHA's Board of Directors.

THE EXPLOSION OF SCIENTIFIC AND MEDICAL KNOWLEDGE in the past century has become a cliché, but it certainly rings true for ASHA's 100 years, which have witnessed breathtaking evolution in sexually transmitted diseases (STDs), especially in the last 50 years. STDs embody all the elements of emerging infections. To start, many of the known sexually transmitted viruses and bacteria have evolved in clinically important ways and entirely new ones have emerged. There is growing awareness of clinical manifestations that could not have been imagined in 1914, even as some complications have become rare. In midcentury the antibiotic revolution offered cures undreamed of through history, rapidly followed by antibiotic resistance that, for gonorrhea, now threatens that very success. Viruses now dominate the STD scene, with their impact only partly balanced by antiviral drugs that offer effective treatment but not cure. As with all emerging infections, accelerating international spread has accompanied the global revolution in travel, population migration, commerce, and communications. Finally, we have come to understand the extent to which transmission and prevention of STDs depend as much on demography, behavior, and culture as on technological advances like improved diagnosis and effective treatment.

EVOLVING STD CLINICAL SPECTRUM, MANAGEMENT, AND PREVENTION

When ASHA was founded, STDs comprised only five recognized venereal diseases (VD), of which only two, syphilis and gonorrhea, were on the plate of public attention and prevention priority. Rudimentary blood tests for syphilis had been available barely a decade and treatment with arsenic compounds was marginally effective, cumbersome, expensive, often unable to prevent life-threatening complications and, as the name implies, potentially toxic. Gonorrhea was viewed as a serious but secondary problem, partly because it was difficult to diagnose in women and because effective treatment was lacking. The rarer chancroid, lymphogranuloma venereum, and granuloma inguinale (more recently called donovanosis) rounded out the recognized spectrum of STDs.

Although chlamydia had been discovered in 1907, understanding of its dominance as the most common bacterial STD was seven decades in the future. The vaginal infection trichomoniasis, genital and anal warts, and "herpes progenitalis" were all recognized. Clinicians knew that urethral discharge in men was not always gonorrhea and referred to it as nonspecific or nongono-coccal urethritis (NGU), but considered it unimportant. Acquisition of these conditions by sexual contact was a matter of debate; while experienced clinicians understood these conditions usually were sexually acquired, they were also adept at explaining away their occurrence with ingenious and sometimes ludicrous reasons why they were not in fact sexually transmitted.

In the 1930s the antibiotic era was launched with sulfanilamide, the first sulfa drug. Although ineffective against syphilis, dramatic results were seen in gonor-rhea, resulting in increased attention to its treatment and the first systematic efforts at prevention. But the world soon became acquainted with the evolution of antibiotic resistance, and by the end of the decade the sulfa drugs were no longer reliably effective against gonorrhea.

War and social disruption have always fostered the spread of STDs, and rates of syphilis and gonor-rhea skyrocketed during both world wars. However, the peaks that accompanied World War II were rapidly reversed by two technological advances: inexpensive, reasonably accurate blood tests for syphilis that were widely deployed in the 1930s; and the introduction of penicillin in the 1940s. No randomized controlled trials were required to immediately understand the dramatic success of penicillin against both syphilis and gonorrhea, and effective treatment transformed both of these STDs from widespread, generalized epidemics that could affect almost anyone to limited transmis-sion within socially and economically disadvantaged corners of society. The 1940s and 1950s also witnessed the first broad-spectrum antibiotics, including the tet-racyclines, which offered effective treatment for NGU and the other, rare STDs, and could serve as backup treatment for syphilis in persons allergic to penicillin.

The advent of effective single dose or short course antibiotic therapy for gonorrhea and syphilis had a long-lasting dark side. In the belief that the STDs would be effectively controlled and even eliminated by antibiotics, there were steep declines in funding of research, and the number of public clinics. Whole

academic departments of "syphilology" were dis-banded because of the expectation that a cure could be achieved quickly and inexpensively by non-specialists in general practice. The resulting decline in brain trust seriously depressed the growth of scientific knowledge and know-how about STDs for three decades.

Thus the United States and other industrialized countries initially were incapable of an effective re-sponse when the "sexual revolution" and other soci-etal upheavals of the 1960s and 1970s led to a virtual explosion of resurgent gonorrhea and syphilis as well as several forgotten and seemingly new sexually trans-mitted conditions and complications. As the 1970s dawned, improved diagnosis of chlamydia was followed by growing awareness of its role in NGU. By the end of the decade, the stupendous frequency of chlamydia and its contribution to fallopian tube infection (pelvic inflammatory disease) and female infertility was also fully understood.

The 1950s and 1960s had seen the glimmer of new knowledge about viral STDs, with the initial description of human papillomavirus (HPV) and the differentia-tion of herpes simplex virus types 1 and 2 (HSV-1 and HSV-2) and their usual associations with oral and geni-tal herpes, respectively. In the 1970s and 1980s these viruses grabbed anxious public attention. Genital herpes emerged as the most feared STD in the United States, owing less to its potentially serious and not infrequent complications than to its high frequency, indefinite persistence, potential for recurrent outbreaks, and lack of effective treatment. Genital warts garnered atten-tion because of their frequency, difficult treatment, and antipathy that probably originated with age-old myths about warts and their origins. Together these STDs cre-ated great apprehension around sexual relationships in an era when sexual activity increasingly preceded personal intimacy. (ASHA arguably was the most effec-tive leader in the nation's response to genital herpes in the 1970s and 1980s.)

Hepatitis B and later hepatitis C, cytomegalovirus (a cause of potentially serious congenital infections in newborns), Epstein-Barr virus (the cause of infec-

THE CHANGING TERMINOLOGY

For ASHA's first sixty years, venereal disease (VD) was the nearly universal term, referring more or less exclusively to syphilis, gonorrhea, and the less common lymphogranuloma venereum, chancroid, and donovanosis. From its earliest use, "VD" had pejorative connotations. Vaginal infections like trichomoniasis, NGU in men, and genital warts and herpes were understood to be associated with sexual activity, but their sexual transmission was a matter of debate, at least partly because these disorders were common in people who seemed to be at low risk for VD.

"Sexually transmitted disease" or STD became the norm in the 1970s, reflecting acceptance of the evidence for sexual transmission of several conditions, discovery of apparently new infections, and increasing awareness that all of these were highly prevalent in the "general population"—implying, at the time, people presumably more responsible in their sexuality than those with VD.

The 1980s began to see increased use of "sexually transmitted infection" or STI. The case was made that most infections caused few or no symptoms and appeared harmless. Even asymptomatic infection with HIV was considered distinct from overt AIDS, and for a decade it was common to inform patients that they "only" carried the virus and did not have AIDS. In addition, some patient advocates considered "disease" to be more pejorative than "infection," and came to view "STD" in a similar light as others had perceived "VD" in earlier decades.

However, time and improved knowledge have partly undercut at least the first rationale in favor of "STI." There is clearer understanding of the often serious outcomes of outwardly silent infections, such as progressive immune deficiency caused by HIV, enhanced HIV transmission because of asymptomatic herpes caused by HSV-2, infertility due to chlamydia, and cancers caused by otherwise silent HPV infections. Arguably, therefore, the distinction between "infection" and "disease" is moot. And there is room for debate about differing connotations of the two words. No reported research has studied whether infected persons interpret the two terms differently. (Such a study would be quite simple, inexpensive, and very welcome!)

Today, "STD" and "STI" are interchangeable. The former *British Journal of Venereal Diseases* is now *Sexually Transmitted Infections*, and the venerable International Union against the Venereal Diseases and Treponematoses (IUVDT) became IUSTI. On the other hand, the American STD Association (originally the American VD Association) retains its name, as do its journal *Sexually Transmitted Diseases* and the Centers for Disease Control and Prevention's Division of STD Prevention. For now the two terms are synonymous and both will continue to be used for some time.

DARK SHADOWS

In 1932, physicians of the United States Public Health Service (USPHS) initiated a research study in rural Macon County, Alabama—whose county seat is Tuskegee—to learn the course of untreated syphilis in African-American men. At the outset, the motivations and attitudes of the investigators were probably reasonable. No funds were available for treatment; the effectiveness of the arsenic compounds then available for treatment was not well established for longstanding, chronic syphilis; and it was believed that the data would ultimately benefit African Americans. (The premise that disease outcomes might be significantly different between racial groups was flawed, but it reflected the scientific consensus of the day.) However, with perhaps well-meaning but paternalistic intent designed to assure long-term compliance and follow-up, the study subjects—most of them illiterate and destitute—were not informed of the true nature of the study and were not offered an opportunity to give consent for repeated examinations over many years. The subjects were told (or at least permitted to believe) that blood collection and invasive procedures like spinal taps were forms of treatment. Most egregiously, when penicillin became available a decade into the study, the subjects were not informed or offered the opportunity for potentially lifesaving treatment, which was withheld for another three decades until a courageous USPHS whistleblower brought the now infamous "Tuskegee Study" to light in 1972.[1]

In the 1940s, the USPHS had been conducting research that included intentional infection of federal prisoners with syphilis and gonorrhea. Given the inherently coercive setting, consent was marginal at best. Fearing adverse publicity and desiring to use inoculation methods deemed inappropriate even in prisoners, the investigators terminated the prison studies, only to begin similar research on a much larger scale in Guatemala. With the knowledge and cooperation of Guatemalan health authorities, from 1946 to 1948 the USPHS research involved ". . . deliberate infection of people. . . without their consent. Subjects were exposed to syphilis, gonorrhea, and chancroid, and included prisoners, soldiers from several parts of the army, patients in a state-run psychiatric hospital, and commercial sex workers."[2] At least one death and uncountable numbers of serious health outcomes resulted directly from the STD inoculation experiments. Some of the same investigators involved in the Tuskegee Study also worked in Guatemala, and senior federal health officials and prominent academics of the day had knowledge and overtly or tacitly approved both projects. The studies continued even after being characterized as "ethically impossible," as the involved officials remained silent and worked to assure secrecy.

The impact of these incidents has been profound. The Tuskegee Study is interwoven into the fabric of race and human rights in America and remains one of the most important reasons for skepticism about health care and distrust of government among African Americans. Ongoing disparities in STD risk, with rates of gonorrhea, syphilis, and HIV/AIDS ten to twentyfold higher in African Americans than in whites, have multiple causes that harken back to the entire history of slavery and race in American society, but the legacy of Tuskegee is a significant element. Addressing racial disparities in STD rates remains a preeminent challenge to the federal, state and local health establishments and ASHA.

Fortunately, there is reason for confidence that a lesson has been learned. Awareness of the Tuskegee and Guatemala experiences, the urgency to solve racial disparities in STD and other health outcomes, evolving attitudes in the health care professions, modern communication technologies, and more open government together give confidence that similar abuses will never again be undertaken or tolerated in the United States. And ASHA stands guard to help assure it.

1 James H. Jones. *Bad Blood: The Tuskegee Syphilis Experiment*. (New York, The Free Press, 1981).

2 Presidential Commission for the Study of Bioethical Issues. *"Ethically Impossible": STD Research in Guatemala from 1946 to 1948*. (Washington, DC, 2011).

tious mononucleosis and certain lymph gland cancers), gastrointestinal organisms like *Salmonella*, *Shigella*, *Campylobacter*, and numerous other bacteria, viruses, and parasites emerged as sexually transmissible pathogens, especially in men having sex with other men.

The nation's awakening to emerging STDs in the 1970s happily coincided with the heyday of federal funding for health research. We began to rebuild the eroded infrastructure for research and prevention, directly leading to the studies that documented the frequency and importance of chlamydia and its complications, especially in women. Re-emergent gonorrhea came back into improved control with new scientific understanding that led to expanded screening and improved treatment. (Of course the bacteria was evolving ever more resistance to antibiotics, requiring repeated changes in treatment that continue to the present day.) NGU in men became the most common single condition diagnosed in public STD clinics, with genital warts and herpes close behind.

Since early in the century, researchers had been postulating that viruses were important causes of cancer, and the prediction found its apotheosis in sexually transmitted HPV. Confirmation of the long-held suspicion of HPV as the cause of cervical cancer, differentiation of more than a hundred sexually transmitted HPV types, the associations of particular types with cancer and genital warts, and the near universality of genital HPV infection made it clear that STDs, far from being restricted to small segments of society, are nearly universal human experiences.

There was some progress against genital herpes as antiviral drugs proved remarkably effective in the treatment and prevention of HSV infections (although curative therapy remains only a dream). Scientists also developed highly effective vaccines against selected strains of HPV as well as against hepatitis B. However, the vaccines' remarkable biological effectiveness is yet to be matched by sufficient uptake in the population to provide optimal prevention. Unfortunately, vaccination against syphilis, gonorrhea, chlamydia, and herpes awaits future research.

THE IMPACT OF AIDS

And along came AIDS, which changed everything. In the 1980s, sexually active young persons of all stripes, STD-prevention experts, and the world at large were shaken from the belief (or at least tacit assumption) that devastating, often fatal STDs were almost extinct and that those remaining would one day succumb to the traditional interventions—diagnostic and screening tests followed by treatment to cure infection and prevent transmission—that had been so successful in controlling syphilis and were making inroads against gonorrhea and chlamydia. The explosive appearance of an incurable STD impervious to biomedical prevention had profound effects, but among the most significant was the wake-up call to the important role that the behavioral and social sciences could play in prevention efforts. Lip service had always been paid to modifying sexual behavior to prevent STDs, but since the 1940s the approach to behavioral prevention could be caricatured as "You really should be using condoms. Now bend over for your penicillin shot."

Forced by the imperative to prevent HIV, there was an explosion of research, investment, and knowledge about the behavioral, cultural, and infrastructural determinants of STD transmission and spread. As it happened, preventing HIV through behavioral interventions—in particular, counseling people at risk to modify risky behaviors—was found wanting. Effective prevention on a wide scale finally became a realistic prospect in the past decade when early detection through laboratory testing could be combined with potent and increasingly available antiviral drugs.

The behavioral and social science reformation of the past quarter century has taught us the importance not only of the behaviors that risk HIV and STD transmission and acquisition, but of the behavioral underpinnings of the biomedical interventions themselves. Who seeks testing for STDs and why? What determines infected persons' communication with exposed partners and how can partner referral be maximized? How can we assure compliance with treatment or other prevention tactics? Once a patient enters care for a chronic infection like HIV, how can follow-up be assured? Further, these sciences have taught us the importance of the behaviors of health care providers and systems. The growing field of translational research—understanding the determinants and maximizing providers' uptake of prevention and treatment recommendations—is, at its core, the application of behavioral and social sciences to physicians, clinics, and health plans.

WHERE DO WE STAND AT THE OPENING OF ASHA'S SECOND CENTURY?

There have been dramatic successes in STD prevention and control in the United States in the past hundred years. Syphilis and gonorrhea are rare compared with 1914, and although both remain rampant in some population subgroups, such as some men who have sex with men (especially those infected with HIV), the large majority of even the most sexually active people will never acquire either of these once dominant STDs. Widespread awareness of the Tuskegee and Guatemala experiences (see sidebar), expanded government accountability, and the revolution in communication technologies—and with ASHA on watch—engender confidence that similar abuses and overtly misogynistic approaches to STD prevention are behind us.

At the same time, the challenges ahead are great. One interpretation of our radically expanded biomedical and social science understanding of STDs is that we know better how far we have to go. In HIV/AIDS, the nation and the world continue to experience the worst STD of all time, notwithstanding dramatic recent improvements in prevention, treatment, and survival.

In contrast to the limited knowledge in 1914, in 2014 we know that most persons are at substantial risk for STD during their teen and young adult years; that at least 80 percent of Americans sexually acquire one or more genital HPV infections during their sexually active years and that many of these infections progress to cause genital, anal, and other cancers; that 15 to 20 percent of the United States population acquires genital herpes; that despite the availability of remarkably effective immunization against hepatitis B and the most troublesome types of HPV, vaccine uptake is woefully inadequate; that gonorrhea could become resistant to most if not all currently available antibiotics; and that each year an estimated six million people in the United States acquire trichomoniasis and three million get chlamydia. Finally, we know that the continuing wide race-ethnicity disparities in the frequency of STDs and their complications—which persist in part because the successes of the past century have not been equitably distributed—will remain at the top of the prevention agenda for the foreseeable future.

The past century has seen astounding progress, to which ASHA has been a key contributor. No doubt that shining success in meeting the nation's great challenges against STDs will continue in the Association's second century.

STDs AND GENDER INEQUALITY

Women are selectively and more seriously affected than men by STDs. This fact does not diminish the importance of STD in men, and in the United States HIV/AIDS, hepatitis B, anal cancer, and sexually transmitted gastrointestinal infections especially impact men who have sex with men. Still, the main significance of STDs in males lies in transmission to their female partners. Most or all STDs are transmitted more efficiently from men to women than the reverse because the vagina retains and prolongs exposure to partners' genital secretions, and the female genital tract is largely composed of more susceptible moist tissues. Women are also especially prone to asymptomatic infection or subtle, difficult to recognize symptoms, and the diagnosis of some STDs and other genital conditions is more difficult than in men, often resulting in delayed recognition and treatment. Most important, female genital anatomy, physiologic factors, and adverse effects on pregnancy render women at greater risk than men for long-lasting or permanent complications, such as infertility, tubal pregnancy, cancer, premature labor, and serious or fatal infections in the children they bear.

Through history, this selective impact of STDs on women has been compounded by sexism both in society at large and among prevention professionals and agencies. In the first half of ASHA's century, some attempts to control STDs were frankly misogynistic. Women in general, and female sex workers in particular, were blamed for transmitting infection and sustaining high rates of syphilis and gonorrhea, as if their male partners had no skin in the game. Women, but rarely men, (except sometimes in the military) were subjected to forced testing, treatment, and sometimes incarceration. Men's sexual drive and need for sexual gratification were taken for granted and even praised. In the name of morale and battle readiness, militaries worldwide—including the United States Army and Navy—condoned and sometimes helped organize brothels near camps and behind front lines, at the same time taking draconian measures against brothel workers when rates of syphilis or gonorrhea in soldiers and sailors rose to unacceptable levels.

The truths of the impact of STDs on women and the ineffectiveness of these methods were known to ASHA at its inception and have been reinforced in recent decades. One of the Association's enduring legacies has been to limit sexist approaches to STD prevention in the early years, and, in recent decades, to redirect prevention in a gender-neutral direction. The culmination of ASHA's evolution in STD prevention is its expanded mission in support of sexual health, broadly defined.

Honest Sex Education: Charting the Course
to a Sexually Healthy Nation DEB HAUSER, MPH

DEB HAUSER, MPH, is the
president of Advocates for Youth.

EVERY HOUR OF EVERY DAY IN THE UNITED STATES 85 youth become pregnant, 425 contract an STI, and two contract HIV. *Every hour of every day.* Yet, 30 years of public health research demonstrates that comprehensive sex education can provide young people with the essential information and skills they need to reduce their risk for unplanned pregnancy and STIs, including HIV. When done well, comprehensive sex education can also help young people traverse puberty, understand the difference between healthy and unhealthy relationships, develop a positive body image, communicate effectively, make informed decisions, and navigate the health care system. In short, quality sex education can go beyond the promotion of abstinence or even the prevention of unplanned pregnancy and disease to provide a lifelong foundation for sexual health.

Comprehensive sexuality education, when done well, can also help shift the culture of fear, shame, and denial which permeates our society and create instead a culture in which sexuality is accepted as normal, natural, and healthy; one in which young people are valued and celebrated for who they are no matter their sexual orientation, gender identity, or gender expression; where sexual development is recognized as an important task of adolescence and education about sexuality is valued over the promotion of ignorance.

One would imagine then, that in the wake of the evidence, policy and practice in support of comprehensive sex education would follow suit. Unfortunately, the United States is home to a conspiracy of silence, shame, and fear that surrounds adolescent sexual health. All too often, politics and ideology trump science, not to mention basic common sense. Since the 1990s, social conservatives have promoted an abstinence-only or "just-say-no" approach to sex education. Deeply rooted in social conservatism, abstinence-only-until-marriage programs are a strategic initiative designed to undermine gains in both the women's rights and gay rights movements. These programs are anti-gay, anti-woman, anti-sex, anti-contraception, and pro-heterosexual marriage. In other words, social conservatives were able to convince the U.S. government to spend more than 1.5 billion dollars since 1998 to undermine public confidence in condoms and contraception, promote homophobia, stigmatize sexuality and sexual development, and inculcate youth with notions of traditional gender stereotypes.

Though we are by no means where we want to be, there has been a great deal of progress in recent years, especially in dismantling abstinence-only programs.

OPPOSITE &
FOLLOWING PAGE: *ASHLEY*

41

By 2010, sex education advocates had helped to eliminate two-thirds of federal abstinence-only funding and to shape two new federal funding streams for evidence-based sex education—the President's Teen Pregnancy Prevention Initiative at $75 million and the Personal Responsibility Education Program at $110 million. By 2012, 14 states and Washington, D.C. had rejected what was left of federal abstinence-only funding, while most states happily accepted the new funding sources. In addition, over the past few years Colorado, Illinois, Mississippi, North Carolina, Washington, and Wisconsin were among the states that passed new sex education laws. In 2013 alone, Alabama, Nevada, and South Carolina also introduced sex education bills (that did not pass but will most likely be reintroduced); the Broward County School District in Florida introduced a new sex education policy that will be voted on in 2014; Chicago Public Schools passed a comprehensive sex education policy which mandates sex education at every grade level; the Tulsa School Board (Oklahoma) voted to implement comprehensive sex education to select schools, with plans to expand across the district; and the *National Sexuality Education Standards* were widely used to fuel sex education advocacy and implementation efforts across the country.

In addition, sex education implementation took a huge leap forward with the launch of the WISE initiative (Working to Institutionalize Sex Education). WISE's goal is to pilot, field test, map, and scale up a strategy for sex education implementation and institutionalization in school districts with positive or neutral policy climates. Currently operating in ten states, WISE is reaching hundreds of thousands of young people each year with new or improved sex education.

Fueled by the success of WISE and the *National Sexuality Education Standards*, in 2013 the CDC's Division of Adolescent and School Health began funding 19 state education agencies and 17 large municipal school districts to implement what it calls *exemplary sexual health education* or ESHE.

All of this is contributing to some success: the teen pregnancy rates have dropped 52 percent since 1991—driven down primarily by young people using condoms and contraception more consistently than ever before. But change has not come easily, nor has it been consistent. We still face rising rates of STIs, including HIV infections, among young people. Improvements in sex education are unevenly spread, and there are pockets in most states, and particularly in the South, where abstinence-only education continues to prevail.

To truly become a sexually healthy nation, we will need to continue to confront the cultural myths that undermine rights, pragmatism, and basic common sense when it comes to sex education in America.

We should start with the myth that education is a threat rather than a solution—the belief that educating young people about sex causes them to have sex continues to prevail. Research has debunked this falsehood for decades but opponents of comprehensive sex education cannot seem to let go of their "umbrellas cause rain" argument.

The second myth is that *just say no until marriage* constitutes a viable national sex education policy in a country where 95 percent of people have sex prior to marriage and 70 percent of young people have sex by the age of 19. Throughout the industrialized world, the average age of sexual initiation is 17. Trying to stop this behavior in its tracks by censoring information about condoms and birth control is not just naïve and ineffective, it's dangerous and irresponsible. Denial will never be a successful strategy when it comes to sex education in America.

We must also refute the idea that young people are incapable of regulating their sexual behavior in a responsible fashion. This "teens run amok" stereotype fuels the perception that young people are problems in the making rather than partners in prevention. Yet despite the characterization, U.S. teens are often more responsible than their adult counterparts (condom use being one example). The bottom line: respect youth and give them the information, education, support, and guidance that they need, and they will act responsibly.

Finally, we must address our conflicted cultural norms around sexuality itself. In America, we use sex to sell everything from laptops to lipstick; we parade advertisements for Viagra and Cialis across TV screens in prime time; and we promote sex-drenched sitcoms during what was once the "family hour." Yet, advertising for condoms during the same time slots is deemed "too controversial" despite the fact that condoms are the most effective disease prevention tool available for those who are sexually active.

On the one hand, young people are being told that sex is dirty, filthy, and disgusting while on the other they are being asked to save it for someone they love. Sex is used for entertainment and commerce but rarely spoken of openly and honestly in our homes, schools, and faith communities. We obsess about what makes us sexually attractive but spend little time educating one another about what makes us successful as partners in a relationship.

Culture will continue to dictate the ceiling for progress on sexual health in America. The sex education our youth get will be decided by how tightly our culture holds on to the fear, shame, and denial promoted by social conservatives and their "just say no" approach. We need to break through this ceiling and provide young people with comprehensive sex education. Only then will we become a society where sexuality is viewed as a normal, natural, positive part of life; where young people are valued as assets rather than liabilities; where public policy is shaped by science and evidence; and responsibilities are properly balanced with rights in a way that empowers young people to become sexually healthy adults.

I don't think it is overstated to say that we have begun to reframe the debate; but how far we go will be determined by our willingness to educate our children—honestly and openly. Only then will we become a sexually healthy nation.

In Between Science and Sonnet:
Sex and Pleasure DEBBY HERBENICK, PhD, MPH

DEBBY HERBENICK, PhD, MPH, is the co-director of the Center for Sexual Health Promotion in Indiana University's School of Public Health and the sexual health educator for The Kinsey Institute for Research in Sex, Gender, and Reproduction. She is also the author of five books about sex and love.

PLEASURE HAS A CURIOUS PLACE IN HUMAN SEXUALITY—it's not always necessary, only sometimes sufficient, and yet often pursued.

Finding sex physically or even emotionally pleasurable is not necessary to human reproduction. People can and sometimes do make babies in planned, rushed ways that are more about timing than feeling. Sexual pleasure is also not needed to have sex that keeps one's partner happy, relieves sexual tension, or facilitates sleep. And, although sexual pleasure and orgasm are often conflated, it is possible to experience one without the other. It is also possible for pleasurable feelings, such as love or enjoyable physical sensations, to be layered in the very same sexual experience with *un*pleasurable feelings, such as shame or guilt. This makes the scientific task of understanding people's reports of whether a given sex act was "pleasurable" quite daunting to say the least.

And yet, that is exactly what many scientists do. We ask about pleasure. Happily, we've found that pleasure is a common characteristic of sex in America. Data from our 2010 National Survey of Sexual Health and Behavior show that nearly all men—about 96 percent—indicated that their most recent sexual experience with a partner was at least somewhat pleasurable. While most women also reported pleasure during sex, considerably more women than men did not; about 14 percent of women said that their most recent sexual experience was "not at all" or just "a little" pleasurable.

In addition, much of the consumer market around sex—sex books, sex toys, lubricants, condoms with special features—is focused around sexual enhancement and pleasure, and ideas that sex "should" be pleasurable. (It's worth noting that many of these products are marketed as enhancing women's comfort and/or orgasm during sex, if not their pleasure.) Though these seem to focus on physical sensations and orgasm, we have to remember that sex is not an ongoing, consistent peak experience, even for the most sexually satisfied couples.

I'm aware, too, that sometimes sex is about physical or emotional survival. And, for many people, sex has to do—at least at times—with maintaining a marriage or long-term committed relationship through a rough spot until you stumble upon a smoother period of joy or contentment.

Indeed, there are many pleasures to be had surrounding sex, and not just in the sex itself. For example, some researchers have highlighted the ways in which people may eroticize the potential for pregnancy, *even if they are*

OPPOSITE: *LYNN AND STEVE*

actively avoiding pregnancy, such as by using condoms or hormonal birth control. Whether or not the sex itself is physically pleasurable, perhaps there are momentary pleasures and joys for some people in imagining how they might make a baby together. As researchers who study sex, it's common for us to ask, "Did you have an orgasm?" but we almost never ask, "Did you, in the midst of sex, imagine what it would be like to make a baby together, and did that feel good?" And yet, what a pleasure that momentary "what if?" can be.

Similarly, we scientists might ask if a person masturbates or has sex "in order to fall asleep," chalking it up as a reason for sex. But making sound sleep a "reason" for sex feels so planned. Couldn't post-sex sleep be one of the pleasures of sex, akin to enjoying a sunrise at the end of a long morning run? Might that sound, dreamless sleep be part of the pleasure, perhaps particularly for people so stressed with their careers or parenting that a night of sound sleep is a long-forgotten luxury? We researchers don't often ask about that, either.

In research and in society, we seem comfortable acknowledging that sex is often pleasurable and that people have a right to engage in it recreationally, not just to make babies. (I should note that this alone has been a hard-won battle, particularly for a society with Puritanical roots.)

Our task now is to expand our ideas and understandings of pleasure—to find ways to capture the myriad pleasures that sex brings to us, whether that has to do with expressing love, sustaining a commitment, feeling young again, making up after an argument, or the physical, sensual pleasures of skin against skin, and inhaling a partner's scent.

This may be where science and art must meet, somewhere in between the pages of a scientific journal and a sonnet, if we hope to understand more fully the very human experiences of what it means to be sexual.

Contraception and Sexuality: Addressing the Pleasure Deficit

JENNY HIGGINS, PhD, MPH

JENNY HIGGINS, PhD, MPH, is a sexual health researcher, advocate, and professor at the University of Wisconsin. Her research explores how a sexual lens can help us improve our classic behavioral models in public health, as well as how to use sex-affirmative approaches to promote the use of condoms and other contraceptives.

Oral contraceptives entered the cultural marketplace 50 years ago and are hailed as a key factor in facilitating the sexual revolution in the United States. Bar none, contraception has improved sexual health enormously in this country—most centrally by helping women and men prevent unplanned pregnancies.

However, whether contraception has led to improvements in women's experiences of their *sexuality* is another matter. Researchers, clinicians, and educators rarely consider the ways in which contraceptives may improve—or detract from—women's ability to enjoy their sex lives. Given that contraception is designed explicitly for use during sex, we know astonishingly little about how contraceptive methods affect women's sexual experiences and processes.

This phenomenon is representative of a larger *pleasure deficit* in the sexual health profession—a lack of attention to the ways in which the positive aspects of sexuality are associated with overall sexual health, especially when it comes to women's sexuality. As individuals, we tend to think about the potential of sex to enhance pleasure or deepen relationships. However, as sexual health professionals, we focus only on the negative outcomes sometimes associated with sexuality, such as STIs, unwanted pregnancy, and violence. The sexual health field's pleasure deficit is especially noticeable when it comes to contraception.

One need only compare mainstream advertisements for contraception with those for erectile dysfunction drugs to see evidence of this. Compared to ads directed at men, which feature couples and suggestions of sex in the near future, contraceptive ads are de-eroticized; they promote contraceptive methods' convenience, efficacy, and non-contraceptive benefits far more than their ability to facilitate enjoyable sex. It has always struck me as odd that our culture uses sexual and erotic images to sell many consumer goods—but not to sell contraception, which is designed expressly *for* sexual activity.

In another example of the pleasure deficit, the majority of contraceptive research and development has failed to collect information on how methods influence women's sexual functioning or enjoyment. Few studies explore current methods' direct effects, if any, on women's libido, enjoyment, arousal, lubrication, or orgasm, let alone how such effects shape contraceptive uptake, continuation, and adherence. Furthermore, researchers have thoroughly investigated contraceptive side effects such as weight gain and vaginal bleeding, but rarely are such changes explored as possible sexual detractors—despite their influence on women's experiences of their bodies, desires, and sexual selves. In contrast, a study of hormonal-based contraception for men that ignored effects on erectile functioning or orgasm would be regarded as incomplete, even invalid.

Programs and policies aimed at increasing contraceptive use can also be marked by a lack of attention to sexuality and pleasure. Current behavioral models of contraceptive decision making suggest that women's choice and consistent use of a particular method are related primarily to access, effectiveness, ease of use, and the desire to limit or space children. Models rarely consider how such methods either enhance or detract from the sexual experience. Moreover, current explanations for *non-use* of contraceptives (which accounts for the lion's share of unplanned pregnancies as opposed to contraceptive failure) pertain primarily to women's knowledge of and access to contraceptive services. Few professionals have suggested that unprotected sex may feel better to women, and/or that pregnancy ambivalence may heighten the sexual experience. Nor do most programs try to market contraceptives by eroticizing them or making them fun and sexy—techniques widely used to improve condom use in the gay community.

Along those lines, we can also see the pleasure deficit in the sexual health field's dominant approach to women and condoms. A significant body of empirical literature documents that many men do not like using male condoms because they curtail sexual sensation, interrupt the sexual heat of the moment, make erections harder to maintain, or undermine other aspects of sexual functioning and enjoyment. The Gates Foundation released a call for proposals regarding the development of more pleasurable and appealing male condoms. The call for proposal stated, "The primary drawback from the male perspective is that condoms decrease pleasure as compared to no condom, creating a trade-off that many men find unacceptable." However, both the Gates Grand Challenge and the majority of current research and programming efforts omit a critical aspect of condoms and pleasure: *women, too, have sexual experiences with condoms, and these experiences*

also shape condom use practices. Until very recently, researchers have rarely considered how condoms affect *women's* pleasure. However, growing research demonstrates that the ways male condoms feel sexually matter to women, too.

An increasing number of researchers are now considering the possible sexual aspects of various contraceptive methods for women, and we're seeing terrific new examples of sex-positive programming and education. My students impress and amaze me with their sex-positive savvy, and I have no doubt that the next generation of sexual health professionals will leave us in the dust with more holistic approaches to sexual well-being.

In moving forward, let's remember that the overwhelming majority of (hetero)sexual activity occurs during times when women wish to avoid pregnancy; and indeed, contraception is expressly designed for non-procreative sexual activity. Further exploring and addressing the sexual aspects of contraceptives would not only lead to a more accurate understanding of sexual health, but also would acknowledge women's capacity as sexual agents and not just "targets" of family planning programs. Let's work from the notion that the way sex *feels* matters to women, and that their sexual risk behaviors—and sexual health and well-being more broadly—will be influenced as a result.

OPPOSITE: *SHAWN, ISAIAH, AND CRAIG*

Have We Finally Given Up on Trying to "Cure" Same-Sex Attraction? MARTHA KEMPNER, MA

MARTHA KEMPNER, MA, is a writer, consultant, and sexual health expert. She is currently a staff writer for the online news site, RH Reality Check, and serves as a consultant to many organizations that focus on sexuality, sex education, and reproductive rights—including, of course, ASHA. Martha served as the editor for this book celebrating ASHA's 100th anniversary and was honored to work with so many dedicated and talented authors.

WITH ALL OF THE GOOD NEWS ABOUT EQUALITY for same-sex couples that we have seen in the last few years, it is almost hard to remember that for the first 60 or so years of ASHA's existence, homosexuality was considered by most people to be a mental illness that should be treated and cured. When this view finally fell out of favor among mainstream medical experts in the early 1970s, a new movement was born—one based on religious beliefs that said homosexuality was a sin, but promised people that with a little bit of "reparative therapy" they could lead happy, healthy, and heterosexual lives. In the decades that followed too many men and women (though mostly men), including young people forced into it by their families, were subjected to this form of "therapy" which has been shown to be ineffectual and dangerous.

Today, as ASHA enters its second century, the science is clear that reparative therapy does not work, many former proponents have admitted as much, one of the largest organizations devoted to this issue has voluntarily shut down, and two states have made it illegal to practice reparative therapy on minors. Is it possible that the days in which homosexuality was considered a problem that needed to be fixed are really behind us?

ONCE A WIDESPREAD BELIEF

Starting with Freud, the modern age of psychology and psychoanalysis viewed homosexuality as an illness. Freud himself believed that everyone had some homosexuality within them but that "normal" people were able to sublimate it. In truth, Freud's views were relatively liberal for the time. He did not believe that curing homosexuality was truly possible and his one attempt to do so within his own practice failed completely. Moreover, he signed a statement in the 1930s calling for the decriminalization of homosexual acts in Germany and Austria. (It wasn't until 2003 that similar laws were deemed unconstitutional in the United States.)

Those who followed Freud in the 40s, 50s, and 60s had many theories as to what "caused" same-sex attraction (domineering mothers were top on the list) and disagreed radically about how to treat it (some thought it would be enough for patients to have a lot of heterosexual sex while others preferred aversion therapy that induced vomiting or shocked a patient with electricity if he got aroused by same-sex erotic images). Of course, most research used to confirm these theories and treatments were done on people who had sought help in the first place.

In 1957, psychologist Evelyn Hooker studied a nonclinical sample of homosexual men and compared them to matched heterosexual men. She found no difference in how well-adjusted they were. Over the next decade, research into sexual orientation continually found few differences between homosexual and heterosexual individuals. Moreover, research failed to support the varying theories that family dynamics, problems with gender identity, or early trauma caused homosexuality.

At the same time, gay rights activists were becoming more outspoken and some were focusing their efforts on changing the Diagnostic and Statistical Manual of Mental Diseases (DSM), which is published by the American Psychological Association (APA) and considered a bible of sorts by practitioners across the country.

Finally in 1973, these advocates—with the help of many inside the APA, including psychiatrist Robert Spitzer who sat on the committee that was charged with updating the DSM—were successful. The mainstream medical establishment would no longer consider homosexuality an illness and practitioners would shift from trying to "cure" patients to trying to help them cope in a world that was still very hostile toward gays and lesbians.

THE RISE OF RELIGIOUS REPARATIVE THERAPY

Some psychiatrists and psychoanalysts remained firmly opposed to this decision. A group of them created a new organization called NARTH (National Association for Research and Therapy of Homosexuality) which was founded on the "assumption that obligatory homosexuality is a treatable disorder." While this organization boasted professional members, a number of other organizations were formed by those with a religious rather than scientific background. One of the most prominent was Exodus International, which was an affiliation of ministries that promoted so-called reparative therapy.

Exodus and 14 other ministries gained national attention in the late 1990s when they launched a million-dollar ad campaign promising that people could "pray away the gay." Proponents of reparative therapy, many of whom referred to themselves as "ex-gays," argued that they were offering a lifeline to individuals who were deeply conflicted by their own same-sex attraction. But their practices were disturbing; some clients said they endured aversive shock therapy that left nickel-sized burns on their arms while others talked about in-patient treatment in which they were left alone for hours and told simply to read the Bible continually.

The mainstream medical establishment was dismissive of reparative therapy from the beginning, but in 2001 the movement found some scientific legitimacy from a most unlikely source. Robert Spitzer, the psychiatrist who argued vehemently for the changes to the DSM in 1973, conducted a study of 200 people who had gone through reparative therapy. Published without peer review in the *Archives of Sexual Behavior*, the paper concluded that most of the participants had successfully changed their sexual orientation.

Many of Spitzer's colleagues denounced the paper as bad science but proponents of reparative therapy hailed it as major victory and seized on Spitzer's reputation and career history as proof that he wasn't biased. They used this study to argue for everything from removing Gay-Straight Alliances in schools to banning gay marriage and civil unions. The ex-gay movement became synonymous with efforts to discriminate against gay and lesbian individuals and couples.

SCANDALS, APOLOGIES, AND SCIENCE

Even as supporters of reparative therapy were reveling in their newfound legitimacy, the movement itself was besieged by a series of scandals. In 2000, a board member of Exodus North America was placed on probation after being photographed in a well-known gay bar. In 2003, an ex-gay actor whose photographs were used in the "pray away the gay" ads was found to be meeting men on the Internet. In 2010, an "expert" on reparative therapy who had frequently testified as to why same-sex couples should not be allowed to adopt children made national headlines when he was found on vacation with a male escort he had hired on RentBoy.com.

Other leaders in the ex-gay movement came forward on their own to say they'd had a change of heart. Michael Bussee, one of the founders of Exodus, admitted that he had been in a relationship with another ex-gay counselor for over 20 years. He offered his sincerest apologies to the gay community and anyone he might have hurt through his involvement with reparative therapy. John Smid, the former director of Exodus affiliate Love in Action, admitted on MSNBC that he is gay and that it is actually impossible to change one's sexual orientation.

Also damaging to the ex-gay movement was a 2009 report by the APA which skewered the practice of reparative therapy. The committee looked at 83 peer-reviewed studies conducted between 1960 and 2007 and found no legitimate evidence that it worked. It said most studies on the subject had serious methodological problems, none were based on credible scientific theory, and many were grounded in theories that could simply never be scientifically evaluated. The report concluded that efforts to change same-sex attraction were not only ineffective but also caused harm including loss of sexual feeling, depression, thoughts of suicide, and anxiety.

And if this report wasn't enough, Robert Spitzer, the author of the one study ex-gay leaders could fall back on, changed his mind as well. In an in-depth interview with the *New York Times* which ran on May 18, 2012, the then-80-year-old Spitzer admitted that his study had a fatal flaw in that there was no way to tell if respondents' self-reports of having changed were accurate. He went on to apologize to the gay and lesbian community and to anyone who had undergone reparative therapy on the strength of his research and reputation.

A year later, an even more shocking apology rocked the ex-gay movement. In June 2013, Alan Chambers, the president of Exodus International, who had also starred in the famous "pray away the gay" ads with his wife, shuttered the organization and posted this apology to the lesbian and gay community on its website: "I am sorry for the pain and hurt many of you have experienced. I am sorry that some of you spent years working through the shame and guilt you felt when your attractions didn't change. I am sorry we promoted sexual orientation change efforts and reparative theories about sexual orientation that stigmatized parents. I am sorry that there were times I didn't stand up to people publicly 'on my side' who called you names like sodomite—or worse." Chambers said that he and his Board planned to open a new ministry that made churches a more welcoming place.

IS THIS THE END?

To be sure, there are still those who believe in reparative therapy. NARTH, for example, still exists and continues to support this practice but between the science, the scandals, and the apologies, the movement has very little momentum and even less credibility. Moreover, two states—New Jersey and California—have passed legislation prohibiting the use of reparative therapy on minors and at least one other is considering it. (A lawsuit challenging the New Jersey law is pending.) Lawmakers in these states agreed that the practice had the potential to cause serious harm.

Hopefully, with all of the information and personal stories we now have at our disposal, we can put the idea of "curing" same-sex attraction to rest forever, and, instead, focus on making our society more welcoming and nurturing of individuals, couples, and families, regardless of their sexual orientation.

We Have a Vaccine that Can Prevent Cancer, but Too Few People Are Using It MARTHA KEMPNER, MA

MARTHA KEMPNER, MA, is a writer, consultant, and sexual health expert. She served as the editor for this book celebrating ASHA's 100th anniversary.

A FEW WEEKS AGO, I FOUND MYSELF in the waiting room of my pediatrician's office talking to a mother who had just decided, based on an email headline she'd seen but couldn't quite remember, not to let her daughter get the HPV vaccine that day. I didn't know this woman at all so I was very cautious in my approach—telling her gently that this was a safe and effective vaccine and urging her to talk to the doctor before making her final decision. In my head, however, I was screaming: "Are you kidding me? We finally have a vaccine that can prevent *cancer* and you're not jumping at the chance to give it to your daughter?" Unfortunately, this woman is not alone. The vaccine has been available since 2006 yet less than a third of eligible young women have gotten all three recommended doses.

According to the CDC, approximately 79 million Americans are currently infected with HPV, and about 14 million people become newly infected each year. Most people who have HPV will have no symptoms or health problems and may never even know they were infected. Some people will get genital warts, which may go away on their own or may need to be removed by a health care provider. But certain strains of the virus, if left untreated, can lead to cervical cancer or cancers of the penis, anus, head, or neck. In fact, it is estimated that two strains of HPV—16 and 18—cause 70 percent of all cervical cancer in this country. Approximately 12,000 women in the United States are diagnosed with cervical cancer each year, and about 4,000 die. (Worldwide, the numbers are much higher.)

Until recently, the best defense we had against cervical cancer was early detection. The Pap test, once called the Pap smear, was invented in 1928 by Greek physician George Papanicolaou. The test scrapes cells from a woman's cervix which are then examined under a microscope by a cytologist who looks for abnormalities that can indicate cancer or precancerous changes. The Pap test allows physicians to catch and treat cervical cancer early or even to detect precancerous cells and provide treatment that can prevent cancer from ever developing. The test is credited with reducing the death rate from cervical cancer in the United States by over 70 percent between 1955 and 1992 alone. In recent years, Pap tests have often been combined with or followed up by HPV screening tests that can look for high- and low-risk strains of the virus. While this is great progress, the rates of cervical cancer have remained unchanged for many years.

In 2006, a new tool in the fight against cervical cancer was introduced in the form of a vaccine that could prevent HPV infection. The first vaccine, Gardasil, protects against four strains of the virus, 16 and 18 as well as 6 and 11, which cause 90 percent of genital warts. A second vaccine, called Cervarix, was approved in 2009 and protects against strains 16 and 18. Though these two vaccines represent major advances in medicine and public health, they have been highly controversial.

Unfortunately, they were introduced during a time when rumors that other routine vaccinations caused autism were running rampant. Though the author of the only study ever to suggest such a link has since been found to have falsified the data for financial gains, the rumors persist and the rates of all kinds of vaccinations have dropped. This generalized distrust of vaccines has clearly affected the uptake of the HPV vaccines as well.

The HPV vaccines also face another kind of opposition because they are designed to prevent a sexually transmitted infection. Some people argue that prevention messages for young people should be limited to "don't have sex" and that giving young people a vaccine is akin to giving them "permission" to have sex. They are particularly concerned because the CDC recommends vaccinations start early (between ages nine and 11), in part, to ensure that all three doses have been received before a young person becomes sexually active. The fear that making prevention methods available—whether vaccines, birth control pills, condoms, or emergency contraception—will cause promiscuity has been disproven over and over again. Research has consistently found that helping young people protect their sexual health keeps them safe but does not change their sexual behavior.

The controversy has meant that many parents, like the woman I met, choose not to take advantage of the protection offered to their children by these vaccines. In fact, only half of eligible girls have gotten one dose of the vaccine and, as mentioned earlier, less than a third have gotten all three recommended doses.

Despite this dismal showing, the vaccine is working—the proportion of teen girls infected with strains 16 and 18 has dropped by 56 percent. This is great news but clearly it could be even better if more parents would trust the research, stop worrying about promiscuity, and get their kids vaccinated. What could be better for our nation's sexual health than a generation without cervical cancer?

BELOW: *ASHLEY*

Porn, Politics, and Public Health   PETER R. KERNDT, MD, MPH

PETER R. KERNDT, MD, MPH, is past Chair of the National Coalition of STD Directors and currently a board member for ASTDA. He is a Clinical Professor in the Department of Medicine, Division of Infectious Disease at the University of Southern California (USC) and an Adjunct Professor in the Department of Epidemiology at the UCLA Fielding School of Public Health. Dr. Kerndt has been principal investigator on numerous CDC and NIH funded research studies and has published over 100 papers in peer-reviewed professional journals.

IN EARLY 2000, WHEN I WAS APPOINTED director of the Los Angeles County Department of Public Health STD Program, LA was, as it remains, the center of the adult film industry. (California and New Hampshire are the only two states where filming of porn has been challenged and declared legal by the courts.) Despite being more than a decade into the HIV/AIDS epidemic, little was being done to regulate the industry or protect performers from HIV or other STDs.

Soon after I started my new position, I was introduced to former porn performer, Sharon Mitchell who was outraged because a male performer had recently admitted that he had knowingly worked after finding out he was HIV-positive, and it had become clear that he had infected five female performers in 1998. Sharon, along with Bill Margold, another former performer, founded the Adult Industry Medical (AIM) Health Care Foundation to bring some accountability and safety to the industry. A colleague and I met with them in the very beginning and began a close, albeit short-lived, collaboration.

After persuading Sharon and Bill that other STDs in addition to HIV were a risk to performers' health, we conducted a study of performers seen at the AIM clinic and presented the findings in 2002 to a gathering of adult film producers hosted by the Free Speech Coalition, the advocacy arm of the industry. None of our findings—including the high rates of STDs—came as a surprise to most performers, who reported that condoms were rarely used and that while they were working, they would be infected with an STD nearly every month. Many would report knowing the signs and symptoms of infection so well that they would self-medicate, accepting their infections as the cost of working in the industry.

OSHA GETS INVOLVED BUT AIM SIDES WITH INDUSTRY

In April 2004, Darren James, a veteran performer who had been tested each month per AIM instructions, would learn that he was infected with HIV. In the 21 days since his last negative test at AIM, Darren had worked with 14 women, three of whom would later learn they too were HIV-positive. No condoms were used in any of the scenes. Personally devastated by the news and the publicity around the disclosure, Darren attempted suicide by drug overdose. Fortunately, he not only survived but has gone on to become an outspoken advocate for performers demanding health-related reforms of the industry.

OPPOSITE: *STEPHANIE AND ANER*

The California Division of Occupational Safety and Health, better known as Cal/OSHA, investigated, and eventually cited and fined, the production company responsible for the workplace exposure of HIV in the James case. That same year, Cal/OSHA released a statement making it clear that workers in this industry were employees protected under the Labor Code and the Bloodborne Pathogen Standard. It also issued immediate guidelines to protect workers that included condom use. Cal/OSHA then held a series of hearings, established an advisory group, and process of developing regulations specific to the industry.

Though AIM and the health department had had a close working relationship since the organization was founded, this all changed after the James investigation. Producers realized that if they did not heed the call to protect workers, there would be further regulation, and AIM sided with the production companies and would never again work freely or openly with the health department. AIM's original mission as an advocate for performers had been transformed virtually overnight and it became the means the industry used to thwart the investigations that would document the exposures and transmission of STDs in the workplace and to shield the production companies from their liability.

Reports of HIV, syphilis, and other STDs transmitted in the workplace continued, and each time the industry responded the same way, declaring a "moratorium" where all performers would be tested. Then shortly afterward, it was always back to business as usual, with no condoms used on sets.

Despite the lack of cooperation from AIM, California law requires that occupation be included in the form used to report an STD diagnosis. The Department of Public Health's STD Program was able to hold AIM accountable by closely monitoring reports that came directly from the laboratory it used. Over the next several years, 25 cases of HIV and thousands of cases of gonorrhea and chlamydia were reported to the STD Program. In 2011, epidemiologist Binh Goldstein, PhD published her findings in the journal *Sexually Transmitted Diseases* and for the first time brought forward evidence of the widespread and frequent reinfection of performers working in the industry.

In May of that year, AIM was forced to close its clinic as a result of operating without a license and a lawsuit challenging its handling of client records. The industry was left scrambling for a new way to show it was taking STDs seriously while a new set of advocates worked to require condoms on set.

AIDS HEALTHCARE FOUNDATION PICKS UP THE FIGHT

In 2007, a colleague and I met with Michael Weinstein, president of the AIDS Healthcare Foundation (AHF). Michael very quickly understood the HIV and other STD health risk to performers and once committed to the effort to change the working conditions was not to be deterred. AHF would use all means available to expose the working conditions and hold accountable those responsible in the industry and those with oversight responsibilities to protect the public's health.

In July 2009, one month after HIV was diagnosed in yet another female performer, AHF filed a petition asking the Los Angeles County Superior Court to order the Department of Public Health to enforce regulations requiring condoms and other measures designed to stop the spread of STDs in this industry. The health department fought the suit, arguing that the adult film industry was not a significant enough portion of its constituency: "the adult film industry employs approximately 1,200 adult performers at any given time and since the population of Los Angeles County is 9,850,000, the health department ought not be compelled to take certain actions in regards to less than 0.01% of the population." This argument won the court case (AHF appealed all the way to the California Supreme Court but lost) but missed the point—adult film performers are not an isolated community, but rather serve as a core transmitter population. As a highly sexually active group with multiple and concurrent sexual partners, this small group is part of a bridge population contributing to a higher rate of disease in the general population of Los Angeles and the surrounding area.

ABOVE & FOLLOWING PAGE: *NADJA*

Frustrated by a lack of progress, AHF appealed directly to the Los Angeles voters, obtaining the signatures necessary to place a measure on the city ballot. After several attempts, in November 2012, Measure B, a landmark voter initiative to require condoms and other safety measures in the filming of porn, was passed by 57 percent of voters. Though in place, the measure is limited and not adequately enforced.

AHF is also working with Assemblyman Isadore Hall, III (D-Los Angeles) on new legislation that would require regular testing of performers and the use of condoms in the production of adult films. AHF has remained a steadfast champion for the cause of worker health and safety in what previously had been a totally unregulated industry.

MOVING FORWARD

Historically, this has been an industry that has operated underground and outside the law hidden from public scrutiny. No doubt there are many in the general public and some in public service who would prefer that porn remain hidden rather than acknowledge and address the conditions and health risks to those working in adult films.

This industry has repeatedly attempted to avoid its responsibility, choosing instead to confuse the public with the argument that this is an issue of "free speech" and to frame the lack of condoms as a matter of "personal freedom." The struggle will not end until employers in this industry are held to the same workplace standards that protect those that work in any other legal commercial enterprise.

59

Sex and the Internet: The First 20 Years DEB K. LEVINE, BSW, MA

DEB K. LEVINE, BSW, MA, is a health educator who began her career at Columbia University with the creation of Go Ask Alice. She founded YTH (youth+tech+health) in 2001, and her work has been celebrated by the White House, the U.S. Department of Health and Human Services, and the National Institute of Medicine.

IT'S HARD TO BELIEVE, BUT IT WAS ONLY ABOUT 20 YEARS AGO that the Internet went mainstream and changed the way people accessed explicit materials, learned about sex and sexuality, and normalized their sexual experiences. Before that, we had to rely on word-of-mouth, X-rated magazines, embarrassed classroom teachers, anxious parents, and chatty friends.

Whenever there is new technology out there, the first thing people do is get involved with sexual content. Whether it was filmmaking, video, or camera phones, before corporations knew what to do with it, people were out there sharing sexual materials. The Internet is no exception. It has played an important role in our ever-changing sexual culture by making available sexual materials, affording privacy, offering perceived anonymity for sexual exploration, and giving us the technology to prohibit developmentally inappropriate access for children and teens. The Internet is a space where people can safely explore their sexual interests, find like-minded communities, and learn about their bodies, fantasies, and desires. Many people who have felt disenfranchised because of their age, disability, gender, or sexual interests, now find community online.

According to our 2011 report, *TechSex USA: Youth Sexual and Reproductive Health in the Digital Age*, today's teens take a multimedia approach to learning about sex—pop culture and reality TV have a huge influence, along with the Internet, social media, friends, family, and trusted brands.

Ninety-three percent of teenagers are online. American youth ages eight to 18 average 44.5 hours per week in front of a screen. Thirty-one percent of teenagers have searched online for information on a health topic that's hard to talk about (drugs, sex, etc.). Nearly three-quarters (73 percent) of online teens use social networking sites. In terms of health, technology is not an end for young people, but a means to accelerate information provision, widen social networks, and sharpen the questions they might ask when they do access health services.

As such, the Internet has also been used as a tool for promoting sexual health and positive messages by social service, public health, and other professionals. There are many sites online that operate outside of the school system to provide comprehensive sex education, information, and advice to youth and young adults (such as Sex, Etc., Scarleteen, and Planned Parenthood's site), and they each have their own strengths and weaknesses. I started using technology myself to teach about sex, sexuality, and sexual health in 1993 when a student asked a wildly complex (and realistic) question about Ecstasy, Prozac, and erections during a dorm talk. In 2014, the site I started, Columbia University's Go Ask Alice, remains a medically accurate, conversational advice column about health, and 75 percent of the questions are still related to sexual health, sexuality, sexual activity, and relationships.

Unfortunately, many teens do not know about these sites, so when they do have a sex question, they simply head to Google and search. Most times these sites are not first in the list of search results, because of a lack of knowledge by sex educators about search engine optimization (SEO) and how teens search online. In addition, in some schools, these sex education sites are still censored. Sex educators and site managers are getting wiser about how to adapt filters meant for young children, how to optimize SEO, and where to send students outside of school in order to ensure teens find accurate, culturally appropriate information.

Public health officials have also learned how to use the Internet as a tool. In 1999, a man came into San Francisco City Clinic and was diagnosed with syphilis. He had had sex with many men but didn't know their names; however, they were all members of the same San Francisco-based AOL chat room. Health officials went into the chat room and alerted chatters that someone in their group had been diagnosed with syphilis and told them about free and low-cost testing services in the city. Nine cases were diagnosed and treated as a result. Today, 12 years later, the Centers for Disease Control and Prevention and the National Institutes of Health have federal programs dedicated to using the Internet, cell phones, and social media for HIV and STD prevention.

I recently co-authored an article in the *Journal of Preventive Medicine* about an HIV-prevention study conducted on Facebook with young adults of color (ages 18 to 24) across the United States. The study found positive short-term results from an eight-week multimedia content driven Facebook page called Just/Us. A play on a private space for "Just Us" and the idea of sexual health as a social Just/Us issue, the Facebook page has over 1,500 friends engaged in discussions of positive sexuality and relationships.

The Internet is here to stay, and so is sex. Whether it's Instagram, Tumblr or the next new thing, rest assured you will be able to find amateur sexual content, explore diverse sexualities and sexual experiences, and find communities of people who like the same things you do. And at its heart, it will always be controversial. People today complain about sexting, censorship, and there's still uproar over access to pornography online. At YTH, we take a different view. We figure as long as people are talking about sex, it's a good thing, and can help advance our culture—not to mention ASHA's agenda—to create a more open, positive view of sexuality and sexual communication throughout the lifespan.

Surviving a Sexually Unhealthy Relationship:
Lessons in Love and Self-Confidence ASHLEY McINTYRE

ASHLEY McINTYRE is a copywriter who lives in Durham, North Carolina. She loves french fries, nonfiction, lazy Sundays with her dog, and whatever Michelle Obama is wearing.

I SPENT SEVERAL YEARS IN A SEXUALLY and emotionally abusive relationship. But I didn't know what was in front of me until a friend handed me a pamphlet on healthy relationships. I read it, and cried. A lot. Not just because I realized that I had to get out, but because I saw that there was hope of being part of a loving couple someday. That's a really cool feeling.

"Allen" and I started out like any high school couple: adorable and awkward. He was the first boy to ask me to a school dance, and we went to every one together until we both graduated. We were inseparable; our love of baseball, good food, and inappropriate jokes kept us attached at the hip. It seemed like a no-brainer to keep things going long-distance when he left to go to college out of state.

We were happy during his freshman and sophomore years. Then he proposed. We were 18 and 19 years old; an eternal commitment to your best friend sounded pretty great, but we had no appreciation for the gravity of the commitment we planned to make. That spontaneous, romantic gesture also left my parents reeling, because he'd neglected to ask for their blessing. My parents still largely supported me financially at the time. In an effort to change my mind about marriage, they confiscated my car and my health insurance card. Ultimately, we decided it would be best to call off the "engagement." Once I gave the ring back, our relationship took a drastic turn for the worse.

Feeling abandoned by my parents, I was just vulnerable enough to believe any comforting thing Allen said. Soon, I was his to manipulate. Although I kept telling myself that I was my own person and could do whatever I wanted, I didn't act that way. We had sex when, where, and how he wanted. If I cried, which I often did, he'd convince me that I "liked it rough," and that "deep down, I really wanted it." He would always say that sex was his way of showing me that he loved me. Then he'd ask me to please forgive him, because he was still learning how to love—to worship—someone as wonderful as me. He made me feel like I was worth nothing without him. At the same time, I felt that he needed me to survive: if I left him, it would kill him. I truly cared about him, but for all the wrong reasons.

When he called, I always picked up. We'd stay on the phone for as long as he demanded, even when I had papers due. My friends hated him, but tolerated him because they loved me; the more honest ones later told me how crass, obnoxious, and sarcastic they found him. They thought he was repressing me, objectifying me, and demeaning me. They were absolutely right; I just couldn't see it.

62

I started to fight back during the summer between my junior and senior years of college, when I accepted a two-month internship in Washington, D.C. Ever since I was a child, I had dreamt of becoming one of those stylish, sophisticated women who lives by her own rules in the big city. Within days of starting my internship, I was lucky enough to connect with a new group of talented, intelligent young adults from all over the country. It was like we had known each other our whole lives. We spent most of our nights together watching the news, running the streets, and discussing how we would change the world when we got the chance. I was living my dream.

And he hated it. I'd go for days without calling; when I did, I would talk about the ambassadors I had met that day, the new international friends I had made, the monuments we planned to see together. Things didn't revolve around him anymore.

We broke up twice that summer, and the second time was for good.

I was able to stay strong after our relationship ended because, for the first time in years, I realized I'd deprived myself of my potential for far too long. I had been given too many gifts, too many talents,

to ignore them for Allen's sake. I was too lucky, too loved, to live in a cesspool of emotional despair. The world was mine, and I needed to embrace it. I finally felt like the beautiful, interesting person I had always wanted to be.

I do wish that my parents had talked to me about abusive relationships when I was growing up. Honestly, I don't think they ever thought they needed to. While it was happening, I shielded them from the truth; sexually and emotionally abusive relationships are often hard to detect in a loved one. As I move forward, I'm learning that surviving an abusive relationship is like surviving a chronic disease; you're never quite cured. You find ways to live with it every day. You relish little victories. You hug people more. You really mean it when you say, "I love you."

Today, I spend my free time practicing yoga, hanging out with my friends, shopping, and whatever else I please. I *have* turned into one of those stylish, sophisticated women who lives by her own rules. My goal at this point in my life is to become as interesting as possible, not for any man, but for my own enrichment. Of course, when my Prince Charming does come along, we'll have plenty to talk about.

Enlightening and Empowering Others FOLASHADE OMISORE, MPH

FOLASHADE OMISORE, MPH, is the senior project manager at the American Sexual Health Association. She is passionate about addressing barriers that lead to social inequality and health disparities.

FOR MANY YEARS, I WAS THE VOICE on the other end of the phone line, wielding the power to end relationships, stop suicide, enlighten, encourage, and empower. I did not ask for this power, but unbeknownst to me it is bestowed upon everyone who answers hotline calls about sexually transmitted infections (STIs) and HIV.

While my training fully prepared me to provide information, I admit I underestimated the impact that information could have on the lives of callers. Though it has been a while since I was the voice on the other end of the line, there are quite a few callers I remember and think about frequently. I wonder what happened after they spoke to me. Were they able to overcome the obstacles set in their way by an STI? Did they still get their "happily ever afters?" Did the information I gave them help?

One call that has stuck in my mind came from one half of "the gym couple," as I still refer them. When I answered, a distraught middle-aged female said instantly, "Tell me how gonorrhea is transmitted." I told her. But then she stated again, "Tell me how gonorrhea is transmitted." So I told her again. Then she asked, "Is that the only way it can be transmitted?" At that point, the light bulb in my mind went off and I knew that what I was saying was not jibing with something she had been told. I began to tread more lightly knowing that what I said might leave this woman's life forever changed. I explained that these are, in fact, the only documented ways it has been transmitted. Then I braced myself for the storm. As expected, the storm built from a few drops of tears to a downpour as the woman began to bawl. After she caught her breath, she told me that she was married, and when she confronted her husband about the diagnosis, he told her he picked it up at the gym. He shrugged it off as simply due to the unsanitary conditions that came along with public showering. I sighed, knowing this marriage had some storms of its own brewing on the horizon as soon as the call ended. When it did, I was left to wonder about the role I had just played.

There were many other callers over the years—those embarrassed to tell partners they had an STI; those needing treatment, but unable to afford it; kids wondering about sex; and those undergoing self-imposed isolation because of their diagnosis who just wanted to talk to someone. Of course there were also the naysayers who believed nothing I said; the conspiracy

64

ABOVE: *STEVE, CRISTIAN, MIRANDA, AVA, AND LYNN*

theorists who swore the government had cures but was saving them only for the wealthy and powerful; and the masturbators who found talking about condoms enough of a turn on to do so during the call.

Some calls made me smile, others made me cry or left me at a loss for words, but I wouldn't change my experience for anything in the world. The opportunity I had to touch so many lives is one not many get to have, and one that many people working in the same position as I did take for granted. There is power in information and for some there is also enlightenment.

I don't know what happened to those I spoke with after the call ended. I will never know, for example, if "the gym couple" worked out their issues of honesty and infidelity or if they are leading separate lives today. I do like to believe that at a minimum callers were better off after speaking with me. My hope is that in our brief call I was able to enlighten them about S T Is and empower them to make informed decisions.

Teen Pregnancy: A Modern Public Health Victory KAY PHILLIPS

KAY PHILLIPS has been working in the teen pregnancy prevention field for 20 years. She began this work as a health educator for the Caldwell County School System and then became the executive director for the Caldwell Council on Adolescent Health. She has been at the helm of the Adolescent Pregnancy Prevention Campaign of North Carolina since 2004.

REDUCING TEEN PREGNANCY HAS BEEN one of the great public health victories of the past few decades. Since the early 1990s, the rate of teen pregnancy has been cut almost in half in the United States and by nearly 65 percent in North Carolina. Just as exciting, our field has transformed into one that is much more considerate of young people's overall health, needs, and rights.

Preventing teen pregnancy isn't about determining who should or should not reproduce or about judging young people's ability to succeed as parents. It's about helping people—starting at a very early age—gain the knowledge, skills, and resources they need to be sexually healthy and happy, and determine when, or if, they will have children. It's also about helping parents, educators, clinicians, and community leaders understand and support adolescent sexual development.

The abstinence-only era of the late 1980s and 1990s gave pregnancy prevention a bad name, funneling billions of dollars and lots of energy into educational programs that relied heavily on shame and inaccurate information about sex, sexuality, and birth control. In North Carolina, that era produced the highest teen pregnancy rates we'd ever seen: for a few years in a row, more than 10 percent of our state's teen girls got pregnant each year. In 2009, we were finally able to change the law to require schools to teach medically accurate sex education that includes information on all forms of birth control.

One of the most exciting trends in helping young people avoid an unplanned pregnancy is helping them access clinical services. Not only are there great new best practices around connecting young people to long-acting methods like IUDs and contraceptive implants, we know more about what makes a clinical setting teen-friendly. (We defeated ourselves and young people for a long time when we would tell someone to go get birth control and then create barriers at the clinic level.) We're also working to help communities support healthier relationships, and understand that relationships can be healthy whether the young people in them are the same sex or opposite sex, sexually active or abstinent. No matter what, sexual health has to include relationship health.

In the end, preventing teen pregnancy isn't about reducing numbers. It's about creating an environment that can produce sexually healthy, happy people who have the knowledge, skills, and resources they need to control their reproductive lives both as teens and as adults.

OPPOSITE: *SHAWN AND CRAIG*

Bridging Generational Divides

CORNELIS (KEES) RIETMEIJER, MD, PhD, & VINCENT RIETMEIJER

CORNELIS (KEES) RIETMEIJER, MD, PhD, is an independent consultant based in Denver. He has worked as an STI researcher, clinician, and teacher for more than 30 years. He is a professor of community and behavioral health at the Colorado School of Public Health. He will serve as the president of American Sexually Transmitted Diseases Association from 2014–2016.

VINCENT RIETMEIJER graduated from the University of Colorado Boulder in May 2014 with a BA in communication.

KEES

In 2006 I saw Amy Schalet speak at the STD Prevention Conference in Jacksonville, Florida about the differences between European and American views on teen sexuality. She argued that parents in the Netherlands "normalize" sexual exploration among teens. They consider it to be a normal part of developing romantic relationships that can be guided and supported within the family and parental context. She explained that Dutch parents would rather know where sexual activities occur and with whom, and that by having discussions with their teen children and their partners they felt some assurance that sexual encounters would be consensual and safe. In contrast, American parents tend to "dramatize" teen sexuality and fear its negative consequences. They insist that teens be abstinent and reserve sex for the safe boundaries of marriage. They tend to avoid discussions on the topic and to the extent that sex still occurs would not want to be associated with it, and thus discourage sleepovers—"not under my roof." (Schalet has an essay in this book that explores the concept more fully.)

I remember the initial response to this work was a mix of enthusiasm and exasperation: surely what appeared to be working in a small liberal country like Holland could not be made to work in a large and socially much more conservative country like the United States.

Yet, in the last few years, trends in this country appear to indicate a normalization of the popular sexual health discourse that would have defied belief a decade ago. For example, the integration of same-sex relationships into the mainstream of American society seemed elusive not so long ago and acceptance of gay marriage a liberal pipe dream. Then seemingly overnight the tide began turning, and now one state after another is changing legislation to allow gay marriage or challenging legislation that doesn't.

Part of the explanation for these developments may be that individuals are changing their minds about these issues. However, a more important explanation lies in shifting demographics as younger generations are coming of age with different attitudes and beliefs than older ones. A recently published report by the Pew Research Center, entitled *Millennials in Adulthood*, found that 68 percent of surveyed Millennials (born 1981–1995) support gay marriage compared to 55 percent of Generation X (born 1965–1980), 48 percent of Baby Boomers (born

1946–1964) and 38 percent of the Silent Generation (born 1928–1945).

While one would hope that the normalization of the discourse around same-sex behaviors extend to other sexual health issues like gender equality, autonomy in sexual decision making, and respect, the point is that what a sexually health nation will look like will be less determined by those who have led the sexual health discourse over the past decade than by those for whom sexual health matters most. In the meantime, the older generations will increasingly become bystanders in the discourse and may be surprised by what their children and grandchildren have to say.

With that, I turn the remainder of this article over to my son Vincent (born 1991).

VINCENT

Growing up in the United States I have found that sexual health and sex education is typically a subject that is avoided when talking to older generations. In my experience, sex has been coupled with other taboo subjects such as politics and religion; a practice that we are expected to engage in, yet one we are expected not to talk about.

However, I believe that younger generations are talking about this in a different way. Within my own generation, I find that people are, for the most part, open and willing to talk not only about the act of sex but about gender issues and sexuality. Today, prior stigmas seem to carry less weight regardless of race, class, or creed. Gender and same-sex equality continue to advance. No longer are these ideas overtly feared. Rather, I would argue that such ideas are becoming normalized and accepted in the minds of youth. I am not saying that acceptance is universal, but its stride seems to be picking up pace.

Nonetheless, it is important to note that these conversations are held predominantly among people of similar age. Young people are not necessarily having these conversations with those of an older generation. It is also by no means a given that they will have these conversations with their own sons and daughters. Normalization of sexuality is not something that should happen just within a generation. Ultimately, it needs to be communicated between generations. Without that, a sexually healthy nation will always be just over the horizon.

BELOW: *JUAN*

Time for Parents to Step Up as Sex Educators, and for Experts to Help Them MONICA RODRIGUEZ

MONICA RODRIGUEZ is the President and CEO of the Sexuality Information and Education Council of the United States (SIECUS).

IN THE SEXUALITY WORLD, THERE IS AN OFT-REPEATED mantra about parents and sexuality education: "Parents are the primary sexuality educators of their children." At SIECUS we've been saying it for most of our 50 years of existence. We say it because it is politic. We repeat it because we want it to be the case. But I'm going to confess a big secret. I don't really think it's true. Don't get me wrong, I wish it were true. I wish more parents and guardians would step up and take an active role in guiding their children when it comes to sexuality. I just don't think many are.

And our children need for it to be true. After all, children start learning about sexuality from the moment they are born. They learn about gender from the way we dress, interact, role-model, and guide them; they learn about biology and anatomy from the way we handle and talk about diapering, body functions, and body parts; they learn about their bodies, pleasure, and boundaries from the way we touch, don't touch, show affection, react to self-touch, and respect (or don't) their preferences and desires about touch and affection. And as they get older, our children learn about relationships, love, sexual behaviors, parenting, and myriad other sexuality-related issues by observing, interacting, and experiencing the broader world.

We live in a country with tremendously high rates of unintended pregnancy and sexually transmitted diseases among young people. In fact, we have some of the highest rates in the industrialized world. While schools struggle to provide basic, factual information about sexuality to students, our children are bombarded, on a daily basis, with verbal and visual media messages about sexuality that range from tantalizing to shaming.

There have been tremendous changes in the last 100 years in how issues of sexuality and sexual health are discussed in the public sphere, but one thing that hasn't changed very much is parents' discomfort in talking with their children about sexuality. Parents and guardians continue to say they feel uncomfortable with the subject and unprepared to tackle it. They worry that their kids know more about the topic than they do. And, they fear that by talking about sexuality they, as parents, are accepting, condoning, or encouraging sexual behavior.

When I talk with parents, they tell me that they want their children to grow up happy, healthy, informed, and to experience good, loving relationships. The brave ones admit that they want their children to enjoy fulfilling, satisfying, plea-

ABOVE: *SOFIA, STEPHANIE, ANER, AND NAIA*

surable sex lives as adults. They also tell me that they feel ill-prepared to help their children get there.

And so, as a result, parents and guardians too often take a back seat and, unwittingly, they allow others—caregivers, teachers, nurses, doctors, therapists, their children's peers, advertising, mass media, even *Sponge-Bob*—to be their children's primary sources of information and values about sexuality.

Instead, I would like to see parents and guardians live up to the mantra of parents as the primary sexuality educators of their children. I want parents and guardians to make sure that they are the ones that get there first and give their children the information, values, and perspective about sexuality that they want their kids to be using as the children grow up and navigate the world. I'd like to see every parent/guardian proactively arm their children with a filter through which they can screen the many conflicting cultural messages they will get about sexuality from the outside world. I want parents to guide their children toward a life in which they can enjoy sexual health and well-being in ways that are appropriate to their age and stage of life.

To parents and guardians, I say step up!

And to those of us working in the sexual health field and to society at large, I say we need to do a better job supporting parents so that they feel knowledgeable and empowered. We need to give parents the resources, information, tools, and support to guide their children toward that life of sexual health and well-being.

Perhaps this should be the focus of our work for the next 100 years.

Can We Stop Dramatizing Adolescent Sexuality? AMY SCHALET, PhD

AMY SCHALET, PhD, is associate professor of sociology at the University of Massachusetts Amherst. Her book, *Not Under My Roof: Parents, Teens, and the Culture of Sex*, has won numerous awards including the 2013 William J. Goode Book Award from the American Sociological Association.

AS A TEENAGER, I WAS VISITING MY NATIVE RURAL New England from the Netherlands—where my family had relocated—when I got a first glimpse of what later as an academic I would call the "dramatization" of adolescent sexuality in the United States. One day, without thinking much of it, I showed the teenage daughter of our hosts a book I picked up at a local second-hand bookstore, Judy Blume's *Forever*. The story of passionate love between two middle-class high school seniors, grappling with the prospect of college away and the looming separation between them, had gripped me.

"Oh, we pass that one around in high school with the pages turned to the dirty parts," said my friend with a combination of derision and delight. It took me a few moments to make sense out of her reaction. I remembered that there was a lot of detail about the couple's lovemaking, but I had not found it particularly striking (other than the two jokingly referring to his penis as Ralph). But it was clear that for my friend and her peers, the forbidden nature of these passages made them so enticing as to eclipse the story about first love and loss.

I could sense the potent blend of emotions that accompanied these underground hand-offs and furtive glances, but not comprehend the culture that fueled them. In the Netherlands of the 1980s—fresh off the wave of its rapid sexual revolution during the previous decades—high-schoolers faced a very different culture. At my school, the Dutch teachers tried to be as matter of fact as possible when they called us into the gymnasium in preparation for our junior year trip to Italy, explaining that anyone in need of condoms abroad should freely ask any teacher—an example of what I have called the "normalization" of adolescent sexuality.

If a Dutch girl had a serious boyfriend, she was usually on the pill *with* her parents' knowledge. So when my friend in Connecticut wrote that she had a boyfriend and wanted to have sex, but did not have birth control, I wrote back pleadingly: "Are you sure you can't talk to your mother about it," followed by a detailed description of when she would be most fertile. I found this letter not long ago when I was cleaning out boxes with materials I saved during the research for my book, *Not Under My Roof: Parents, Teens, and the Culture of Sex*, a book born out of the question raised by growing up between two countries: why the difference?

My research took me deep into the workings of culture and the different ways adults in the two countries think about teenage sex, love, and autonomy: Dutch

ABOVE & FOLLOWING PAGE: *JENNIFER*

parents try to protect by keeping tabs on and managing the risks of sex in the home, permitting older teenage couples to sleep together; American parents try to protect by preventing sex, which in turn drives teenage sex away from the home and makes it harder to control. The Dutch strategy is not perfect but it allows teens to reconcile their sexual selves with their roles as daughters and sons. American teens, especially girls, have to separate the two, thus leaving them more at the mercy of their peer culture.

As much as the differences in teenage pregnancy rates—which are much higher in the United States than in the Netherlands—compel attention, it's the psychological costs of the culture of secrecy in the United States, so apparent in cross-cultural perspective, which seem to spur the strongest reactions in audiences when I present on the book. One of the great-

est satisfactions of my work has been to hear parents say my research has prompted them to rethink their approach—opening conversations, if not permitting sleepovers—and that they feel closer to their teenagers as a result.

These parental disclosures make me hopeful about the prospects of cultural change here in the United States. At the same time, families aren't islands. And in the absence of support from society at large, American parents who go against the grain of decades of dramatization may feel stigmatized or even ostracized. Organizations like A S H A—with its apt message "take the shhhh out of sexual health"—help contribute to a climate in which the next generation of parents can be more comfortable addressing issues of sex, relationships, and health with their children.

Classrooms without Walls: Using Technology to Better Reach and Teach Young People ELIZABETH SCHROEDER, EdD, MSW

ELIZABETH SCHROEDER, EdD, MSW. is an award-winning educator, trainer, and author in the areas of sexuality education pedagogy, LGBTQ issues, working with adolescent boys and the use of technology and social media to reach and teach young people. She is the former executive director of Answer, a national sexuality education organization.

SEXUALITY EDUCATION HAS BEEN PROVIDED IN ONE SHAPE or form to young people in the United States since the beginning of the 20th century. Mostly offered as "moral," "hygiene," "puberty," or "family life" education, the earliest forms of sexuality education featured two core elements from which all subsequent sexuality education has morphed and to which almost all programming continuously returns: a) the prevention of pregnancy or disease and b) the idea that heterosexual marriage is the only acceptable context in which people should engage in sexual behaviors.

Ironically, while so much has changed over the past century, we are still addressing sexuality as if it were the 1920s. We have made progress, to be sure, but at a far slower pace than young people in this country need. The current generation of young people has significantly easier access to far more explicit sexual imagery, not only through the accessibility of pornography on the Internet, but also through cable (and in some cases, regular) television programming. Yet to teach medically accurate, age-appropriate, information and skills in schools, we often have to fight tooth and nail. This must change.

For more than 30 years, Answer has been part of the fight to have science and best practices trump political ideology from social conservatives who are in deep denial about the sexuality realities young people face today. Even in states with supportive sexuality education mandates, and in communities where schools and parents work in collaboration to ensure young people receive the sex education they need and deserve, what young people are receiving is not enough. We must supplement school-based sex education with unfettered, direct access to sexuality information using a free, accessible tool: the Internet.

The dawn of the Internet saw the creation of Answer's award-winning website, Sexetc.org, which provides a fully interactive, online sexuality education experience for youth. Connected with our social media platforms, Sexetc.org reaches young people wherever they are on laptops and mobile devices. No matter where, no matter when, young people can receive answers to the questions they have on absolutely any sexuality-related topic.

We need to fully embrace technology and social media, which have been invaluable tools for ensuring that young people have access to sexuality information and resources. The key to ongoing success in reaching teens where they are will be to stay current with whatever technologies appear next on the horizon.

That said, we must be sure that the technology we embrace fits our mission and goals. For example, when organizations around the country began implementing texting campaigns for young people to text sexual health questions, Answer was asked whether it would be doing a similar campaign. Although many organizations have had success, particularly in connecting young people with health services, Answer chose not to do a texting campaign because the questions young people ask tend to be too complicated to reply in just a few words. So while it is tempting to jump on the bandwagon of the latest technology or service available, particularly if funders are excited about them, organizations should not do so without thinking about their rationale for using a particular type of technology or social media outlet, the fit with their mission and programs, and the intended goal.

We have made progress, but we still continue to play catch up—and that has to stop. As long as federal and state funding is wasted on abstinence-only-until-marriage programs, comprehensive sexuality education programs in schools will be forced to do the double duty of un-teaching misinformation before they can teach the information young people need and deserve. As long as communities resist teaching even the minimum, essential content as recommended by the *National Sexuality Education Standards, K-12*, young people will be misinformed by porn and other sexually explicit media. We have—and must take advantage of—the opportunity to use technology to reach young people outside of the classroom. There is too much at stake to do anything else.

Baby Boomers Getting Older but Not Giving Up on Sex

PEPPER SCHWARTZ, PhD

PEPPER SCHWARTZ, PhD, is a professor of sociology at the University of Washington in Seattle. She is the past president of the Society for the Scientific Study of Sexuality and the author of 20 books, most of which are about sexuality and/or relationships.

LIKE OTHER BABY BOOMERS, I HAVE BECOME EXQUISITELY EXPERT at denial. I am not sure how it came to pass that those of us born roughly during the period of 1945 to 1964 thought we might never have to age—but somehow we did. Even though we know, deep in our hearts, that Ponce de León never found that fountain of youth, there is a petulant part of us that strongly resents any infringement on our youthfulness.

Nowhere is this more sensitive than when it concerns our body's appearance and function—and you can double that sensitivity when it comes to sex. After all, sex was the hallmark of this generation's adolescent rebellion, and later on, a part of the women's movement we spearheaded. We supported more (and better) sex in movies, television, and magazines. Boomers may not have started the Stonewall uprising, a landmark event of the gay civil rights movement, but we have been part of the movement's leadership and backbone.

Speaking of progress, though the famous sex researchers Masters and Johnson were not Boomers, their research emboldened us to ask for more out of our sex lives . . . and we did. Boomers fueled the growth of sexual freedoms, sexual aids, and, ultimately, sex therapy. We have been part of a demand for sexual enhancements that include vibrators, lubricants, and drugs for erection and desire. We equate sexuality with vitality. (The initials ED are now understood by almost every man on the planet.)

So it's not surprising that surveys find that the vast majority of older men and women not only believe sex is important but also maintain an active sex life. A majority of them are willing, if not eager, to see what they can do to continue to be sexually active for as long as possible.

But the demand for lifelong sexual ability is not always easy. Sexual desire, loss of partners, and discomfort with aging bodies can get in the way. Women's sexual desire and arousal after age 50, for example, can be complicated and there does not seem to be a magic elixir that will prop up women's ardor in the same way erectile dysfunction drugs, shots, or pumps can prop up a penis. Too many older adults, and in particular too many women, feel defeated by a lack of sexual interest, pleasure and/or comfort with their body.

Many men and women over 70 are alone. Not knowing how to find a partner or lacking the courage to go online and look for one, they get dispirited, depressed, or just turn off their sexual engine as a rational adjustment to their situation.

Moreover, the sexual health and sexual knowledge of older adults who find themselves back in the dating scene is not too impressive. Two surveys released in 2010 found that less than one-sixth of older single men and only about one-third of older single women used condoms consistently or always. Condom use is almost invisible among single older adults, even though some are now so thin (but strong) that many men aren't sure they are still on! Not surprisingly, the number of people over 50 with sexually transmitted diseases has been going up.

So, older adults, the same people who sparked and maintained a sexual revolution, are having to reinvent themselves again. They are having to deal with the side effects of some medications used to combat major illnesses, like depression, cancer, and vascular diseases, which can affect their sexual health. They are forcing themselves to recognize the fact that afflictions of older people (diabetes, heart problems, high blood pressure, etc.) may eventually surface in their lives and sex lives. They are trying to figure out how to deal with bad knees or backs without letting these aches and pains undermine their sexuality. They are often dealing with the issues that come with living in retirement communities or, later, nursing homes. And, they are having to deal with the real consequences of STDs.

All that said, it is a brighter world for the sexual lives of Boomers and their elders than it was for people who are now in their 80s and older. There are all kinds of sex therapy, some great (and alas, some not so great), as well as all sorts of information on the Internet that is accessible to anyone, not to mention more and better sex research and advances in sexual medicine.

These are steps in the right direction and give us reason to be optimistic about a longer sexual life cycle for older people now—and in the future.

BELOW: *ZOLTAN AND EVA*

The Invention of Prevention MAMTA SINGHVI, MD

MAMTA SINGHVI, MD, is a proud Bruin, having received both her BA and MD from the University of California, Los Angeles. She is currently a resident in radiation oncology at UCLA. Her other interests include yoga, running, cooking, writing, and traveling. She also is an avid college and professional basketball and football fan, courtesy of her older brother.

SEXUALLY TRANSMITTED INFECTIONS (STIs) ARE ILLNESSES that are transmitted from human to human by means of sexual behavior, including vaginal, anal and oral sex. Until the 1970s, STIs were commonly known as venereal diseases (VD), derived from Venus, the Latin word for the Roman goddess of love. Any intimate behavior that involves contact with another person's bodily fluids harbors some risk of infection. Some of these same infections can be transmitted by direct skin contact, while others can also be contracted by IV drug use or even through childbirth. It is important to remember that these illnesses are transmitted from an infected person to another, as opposed to actually being caused by the sexual activity itself.

Prior to the advent of modern medicines, STIs were considered incurable, and treatment was limited to treating the symptoms of the disease. Mercury and arsenic were commonly used, which often resulted in lethal side effects. Because of the associated stigma, however, people would frequently hesitate to seek aid while continuing to transmit the infection to unwitting sexual partners. To promote voluntary treatment, the first official VD hospital was founded in 1746 in London. By the second half of the 19th century, coercion came into play with the British Contagious Diseases Acts, which were used to arrest and treat suspected prostitutes. Soon thereafter antibiotics hit the scene, and a large number of bacterial STIs suddenly became curable. This watershed development led the general public mistakenly to believe that STIs were no longer a serious medical threat.

Then in the 1960s and 70s we saw a change in social mores, resulting in a dramatic increase in adolescent sexual activity. This behavior translated to widespread infection among younger age groups. It was during this period that the importance of contact tracing was recognized. By tracing the sexual partners of infected individuals, testing these partners, treating all of the infected persons, and tracing their contacts in turn, health clinics could effectively suppress and even prevent infections in the general population. Unfortunately, despite these efforts, the late 20th century witnessed an onslaught of viral STIs, such as HIV/AIDS and genital herpes, that were incurable. It was the 1980s AIDS epidemic, in fact, that led to a focus on preventing STIs and heightened calls for safer sex practice.

Safer sex is a strategy aimed at reducing, not eliminating, the risk of transmission, and it is only effective at preventing the transmission of STIs if both parties commit. The term includes a variety of measures, such as limiting the

ABOVE: *FOLASHADE*

number of sexual partners (especially concurrent partners), using condoms, avoiding the exchange of bodily fluid, and resisting the use of drugs that promote high-risk sexual behavior. Abstinence is the only sure-fire way to prevent sexual transmission of diseases, although it is worth repeating that infection is possible through other routes including blood transfusions and breastfeeding. Moreover, evidence does not support the use of abstinence-only sex education, because this remains an unrealistic expectation.

Contraceptive methods, such as birth control pills or tubal ligation, are effective at decreasing unplanned pregnancy, but are of no use in preventing the spread of

STIs. Condoms, however, provide excellent protection against the spread of STIs as they have been proven to reduce the risk of transmitting those infections caused by exchange of fluid as well as those caused by skin-to-skin contact (so long as the infected skin is in the area covered by the condom).

The fact remains that prevention is the key to combating sexually transmitted illnesses. Public health campaigns and community- and school-based education remains critical. Nonprofit organizations such as ASHA have been at the forefront of these efforts for decades, and this dedication to the cause will be paramount as we enter the next centennial.

Political Pushing and Pulling: Ongoing Debates over Sexual Health and Rights WILLIAM SMITH

WILLIAM (BILL) SMITH is the Executive Director of the National Coalition of STD Directors (NCSD) and a Senior Faculty Fellow at the Robert Wood Johnson Center for Health Policy at the University of New Mexico. He is also a PhD Candidate in Politics with a focus on political philosophy and the American Founding.

TO BE SURE, THE POLITICS OF SEX IN THIS COUNTRY isn't just a practical narrative in which one policy or program dominates or obliterates another. Rather, it tells the protracted tale of two diverse worldviews that were with us at the very founding of the nation and persist to this day. One, a view that looks over the shoulder, lamenting how wonderful everything once looked, and attempts to slow or even reverse the "decay." The second, a stern stare back into that same past that finds injustice, inhumanity, and inequity, and ultimately tries to set a course for determining a "better" future. In between those two poles is where most Americans live and breathe and it's where we have been debating sexual and reproductive health and rights for the last century if not longer. To capture all of the struggles in the last 100 years is the feet of a tome, not a short essay. So let me, instead, choose a few issues that seem timeless as "great good work," in Abraham Lincoln's noble words, and review efforts to secure our sexual and reproductive health and rights.

First, the issues of privacy and confidentiality remain as relevant as ever. In 1965, the U.S. Supreme Court issued its landmark decision of *Griswold v. Connecticut* which allowed married couples to access contraception and has since become the foundation for much of our sexual and reproductive rights. It's the basis for extending the right of privacy in contraceptive use to unmarried couples (*Eisenstadt v. Baird)* and for the *Roe v. Wade* decision legalizing abortion. It also lay the groundwork for granting rights to gays and lesbians first through the Supreme Court's 2003 ruling in *Lawrence v. Texas* which overturned discriminatory laws banning same-sex sexual behaviors and more recently through the decision to strike down parts of DOMA (the Defense of Marriage Act). The courts have helped pave the way for a true culture shift that has opened the door to marriage equality in many states, something I honestly never dreamt of as being possible as a gay kid growing up in rural Pennsylvania.

Yet today, there are new challenges to the right to privacy that threaten access to reproductive and sexual health care services. Not the least of these is the transforming nature of the healthcare delivery system, and more specifically, the technology that maintains our healthcare records and the insurance companies and government agencies that handle our claims. Less legalistic and more practical, the issues are who has access to your health records and their contents. Does a dermatologist's office get to see your STD test results from the public health clinic? Does your gastroenterologist get to see your family planning consultation records? If your health insurance company is sending an explanation of benefits statement, will it disclose sensitive information—for example, an HIV test? Should parents have access to medical records for minor children or for older children remaining on their parent's health plans? And if so, what contents are kept confidential and how do we create and manage those firewalls? These are solvable issues, but not without their own set of challenges.

While privacy in healthcare has always been of genuine concern, the expansion of health care in the United States brings new perils and challenges for advocates. The Affordable Care Act—Obamacare for those embracing the term—in its extension of health insurance coverage for millions of Americans, its elimination of discrimination on the basis of pre-existing conditions, and its mandate to cover certain preventive services without a copay or deductible is to be lauded. A number of the covered preventive services involve sexual health including birth control, Pap tests and cervical cancer screenings, and testing for STDs such as chlamydia and gonorrhea for certain populations. Again, these are good things especially when patients take advantage of them, but it means an ever-greater degree of vigilance must be maintained at all points where privacy and confidentiality could be compromised.

The second greatest political issue of our times is sex education, which seems as intractable in this country as abortion. It is a mini-stage on which the nation's sexual dissonance plays itself out on the shoulders of young people whose very lives and livelihoods depend on getting the right information. One side going back to the "good old days" where they claim no one had premarital sex and everyone lived happily-married-ever-after. The other hoping to address inequalities based on gender and sexual orientation and prepare young people for today's world.

Worse still, under the guise of a truly historic and largely laudable effort to address the global HIV/AIDS threat, the George W. Bush Administration exported our home-grown abstinence-only-until-marriage nonsense in the humanitarian relief of the President's Emergency Plan for AIDS Relief (PEPFAR). This has had generational consequences in countries that are most impacted by the pandemic. Sadly, too many years went by as billions of dollars in federal resources were squandered on a hypermoralistic "just say no to sex" approach.

Though it may seem like those days are in our country's rearview mirror, the federal government still hands out 50 million dollars per year in abstinence-only-until-marriage funding. And yes, while new teen pregnancy prevention funding outpaces what is spent on abstinence-only-until-marriage programs, policymakers have brokered a bitter deal that essentially allows both programs to exist side-by-side in an uneasy, irreconcilable truce. Further, as history has taught us, a complete turn of the tables is but an election away.

It is also disappointing to note that while advocates have long championed a truly comprehensive approach to sex education, the programs created under the Obama Administration, and as a counter balance to the abstinence-only approach of the previous Administration, are lamentably still stuck in disease- and pregnancy-prevention paradigms. In many ways, the sex education debate is a place in which "political" policy makers always take the path of least resistance.

There is much that still needs to be done to further sexual and reproductive health and rights in this country, and indeed, given our diverse and vast republic and its citizenry, this may always be the case. Advocates will always be needed because it's not just about making progress, but equally about holding back assaults on things once considered secure. As the one side seeks to correct the social injustices it sees in the past, the other will continue to argue that things were better then. That in 2014 we continue to fight for the right of women to access contraception is but one example to illuminate the never-ending pattern of political pushing and pulling. Again, to quote Lincoln, we need to continue the "great good work."

STDs: Moving Forward Without the Shame and Social Stigma

JO VALENTINE, MSW

JO VALENTINE, MSW, is the Associate Director for the Office of Health Equity in the Division of Sexually Transmitted Disease Prevention at the Centers for Disease Control and Prevention. In this role she leads the efforts to reduce STD disparities in the United States.

WRITING ABOUT THOMAS PARRAN'S EFFORTS to address the rampant sexually transmitted disease (STD) epidemics in the 1930s, Allan M. Brandt noted in his book, *No Magic Bullet: A Social History of Venereal Disease in the United States Since 1880:*

> *The debate over how to identify venereal disease reflected two related themes. First, it signified an attempt to reduce the moral stigma attached to these infections in order to make it possible for physicians to deal with them more dispassionately, in a manner similar to the way other infectious diseases were approached. Second, it revealed a larger conflict over the jurisdiction of these ailments. Passed from the theologian to the social reformer, the concern over venereal disease, it was argued, should henceforth be placed exclusively in the domain of the physician. This, of course, reflected a more fundamental transformation regarding sexuality in American culture.*[1]

That transformation arguably is still underway today, and ASHA remains in the forefront. Sex, and therefore sexual health, in America can at times seem as controversial now as it was a century ago, with an enduring tension between what is medical and what is moral. In the book, *Intimate Matters: A History of Sexuality in America*, the authors noted that sexuality is constantly reshaped by "the changing nature of the economy, the family, and politics."

We must also note the additional influences of social stigma and shame, which have always been associated with STDs, factors that cloud the lens through which society sees these infections and their sufferers. As early as the 1930s, in an effort to bring what was then referred to as *venereal diseases* out of the shadows of medicine and whispers of polite conversation, Parran warned us about syphilis specifically, "First and foremost among American handicaps to progress against syphilis is the widespread belief that nice people don't talk about syphilis, nice people don't have syphilis, and nice people shouldn't do anything about those who have syphilis."[2] While certainly a bold statement nearly eighty years ago, it is arguably also bold today.

And perhaps there is no more profound example of the negative impact of social stigma and shame than in the case of African Americans who have often borne the greatest burden of disparities in STDs throughout history. As one early 20th century physician warned, "The gravest problem to be faced in dealing with the Negro is not his or her industrial future or right to social equality with the white

ABOVE: *FRED*

man or woman. It is the danger to the public of his or her contagiousness and infections from the standpoint of physical and moral disease."[3] In this example, the entire African-American population, both the sick and the healthy, was declared to be a threat to white American society based on its moral and sexual health. Even as recently as 1992, a researcher examining the biological determinants of adolescent sexual behavior wrote, "In the U.S. the sexual activities of white males, and of blacks of both sexes, are a close reflection of the level of testosterone in their bloodstreams for any given period. Thus for these groups early puberty predicts early sexual involvement. White females, however, are far less responsive to hormone levels and are far more responsive to the societal rules and psychological considerations."[4] Old social stigmas and racial biases seemingly die hard.

Yet despite the controversies still associated with sex, sexuality, and sexual health, there has been significant progress in the field of S T D prevention and control, and since 1914 A S H A has been a vital leader in the effort. We now understand sexual health in ways that are enabling us to better balance intervention strategies to promote healthier individual behaviors while at the same time improving the broader social determinants of health. There is certainly more work to be done, but as we move forward it is valuable to review the lessons offered from past attempts to address these ongoing health challenges.

We all have an interest in S T D prevention because we all are impacted by S T D s directly or indirectly, and yet the primary hurdle, even today, remains the difficulty of openly confronting issues surrounding sexuality and S T D s in the United States. The balancing of public and private interests in morality, clinical care, and public health is the transformation that must continue. Fortunately A S H A will continue to help lead the way forward.

1 Allan Brandt, *No Magic Bullet: a Social History of Venereal Disease in the United States since 1880,* (New York: Oxford University Press, 1985).

2 Thomas Parran. "The Next Great Plague to Go," *Survey Graphic* 25 (July 1936):405–411; and "Why Don't We Stamp Out Syphilis," *Readers Digest* (July 1936) 65–73.

3 Nick J. Meyers. *Black Hearts: The Development of Black Sexuality in America.* (Vancouver, Canada: Trafford Publishing, 2003).

4 Carlfred Broderick. *Marriage and the Family, 4th edition.* (Englewood Cliffs, NJ Prentice Hall, 1992).

Let's Keep Talking About Sexual Health FRED WYAND

TALKING ABOUT SEX AND SEXUAL HEALTH in a meaningful way doesn't come naturally for most of us, partly because no one really coaches us on just *how* to have these conversations. Here are four sexual health conversations most of us will need to have at some point, and some pointers on how to have them.

YOUR HEALTH CARE PROVIDERS

If your health care provider doesn't start the conversation, then by all means you should. Even if you have no obvious concerns, let your provider know you want sexual health to be a regular component of your wellness visits. Start by asking for his/her expertise: given your age, sex, medical and sexual history, are there screening tests or vaccines recommended for you? Then think about what advice you might need. Are you happy with your sex life? Do you need help coping with some aspect of your relationship? Talk to your provider—he or she should be able to help. (If your provider seems uncomfortable or dismissive, perhaps you should find a new one!)

YOUR PARTNERS

There are so many things that partners need to talk about when it comes to sex, from negotiating contraception and disease prevention to figuring out what each person likes and doesn't like. Not getting something from your partner that you want? She or he may not even realize there's an issue. In a way that doesn't blame or demand, simply let your partner know what feels good, what makes you happy. Check in about his or her own needs, too. It's much easier for your partner to take care of you if he or she feels it's being reciprocated.

YOUR KIDS

Rule number one when talking about the birds & the bees with your kids: be available. Let them know it is okay to come to you with any questions or worries they have about relationships and, yes, sex. Don't bury your head in the sand; the entire human race discovers sex during the teen years and your job isn't to lock your children up until they turn 21, it's to make sure they know how to protect and stand up for themselves and their sexual health.

YOUR PARENTS

This is one talk that people often don't think of—as adults we can imagine talking about sex with our kids, but our parents? Yet, as your parents age they may lose a long-term partner and find themselves active in the dating world. It may not occur to them to practice safer sex (the first time around, unintended pregnancy, not STIs, was probably their main worry, and that's not a concern anymore). If mom or dad is making the scene for the first time in a while, don't be shy about letting them know they still need to use protection.

FRED WYAND is ASHA's director of communications. Since 2003, he has directed ASHA's HPV and Cervical Cancer Prevention Center and has served as editor of *HPV News*. He has developed a number of resources about STIs for diverse audiences, including patients and health care providers, and serves as project manager and co-developer on ASHA's CME programs.

OPPOSITE: *MARIA CARMEN*

84

The Rise and Fall and Rise of IUDs SUSAN WYSOCKI, WHNP-BC, FAANP

SUSAN WYSOCKI, WHNP-BC, FAANP, a woman's health nurse practitioner since 1975, is a pioneer of the profession. She is a speaker, writer, consultant, and advocate for women. For 25 years, she grew an organization that represents nurse practitioners providing care for women. She is currently the President of iWomansHealth which provides insight, information, and interconnections between experts, clinicians, and women.

I BECAME A NURSE PRACTITIONER IN 1975. At that time, IUDs—which had been around in some form or another for centuries—were "go to" birth control options for women of all ages. However, real safety concerns about one model—the Dalkon Shield—were starting to emerge and ultimately they would change the history of this birth control method for decades to come.

The Dalkon Shield was more difficult to insert, more painful to remove, and carried a high risk of infection. As time went on, we learned that the string on the Dalkon Shield, which was constructed with multiple, combined, plastic threads, was the problem. These multiple threads acted like a wick to bring bacteria into the uterus.

This device became the subject of a multi-billion dollar class action lawsuit that tainted all IUDs, despite the fact that the problems were exclusive to this model. The IUDs I used did not share the same problem of a wicking string. I can say with confidence that even the youngest patients I provided with IUDs did quite well and were very happy with their method. Nevertheless, in the shadow of the Dalkon Shield, these models were also taken off the market and it was many years before a company would introduce one again.

The hiatus meant not just a public that was misinformed about the safety of new devices as they were released but a medical field in which few practitioners had the training they needed to insert or remove IUDs. Even when the devices became available once again, many patients and practitioners shied away from them and they were only ever used in older women who had already had children.

Today, we have several IUDs, or as they are referred to now, intrauterine contraceptives (IUCs), on the market. These IUCs are completely reversible, yet as effective as sterilization (getting tubes tied, etc.) for preventing pregnancy. Once the device is removed, a woman's ability to become pregnant is the same as it would have been at her age had she never used an IUC.

IUCs are a mainstream contraceptive for any woman of reproductive age, including young women. The American College of Obstetricians and Gynecologists has declared them to be a first-line choice for adolescents and young women. In fact, a new smaller version of a popular IUC has been recently released and is aimed specifically at adolescents and young women.

IUCs are particularly appealing for women who do not want to think about contraception on a daily, monthly, or even quarterly basis. With their "set it

and forget it" mode of operation, I U C s take user error out of the equation. Some public health experts see widespread use of this method among young women as a way to prevent virtually all teen pregnancies. (Of course, this method does not provide any protection against S T D s and it is important that young women and their partners understand that limitation.)

Unfortunately, the shadow of the Dalkon Shield has not completely cleared despite the passage of decades.

Many consumers don't know about this method and others have misperceptions. Still, data shows that the method is slowly gaining popularity with women using contraception. And, more and more healthcare providers are being trained in the easy insertion and removal of the devices.

It is clearly a new dawn for this highly effective method of preventing pregnancy.

Thank you to all those who were interested in being in the book. It adds the perfect touch since sexual health really is about people, all people.

Ava Grace Alupului	Sophia Goss
Cristian Alupului	Donald Craig Johnson
Carlos Arteta Rodriguez	Lauren Johnson
Juan Aviles Rosario	Isaiah Johnson-Long
Lynn B. Barclay	Sheldon Johnson
Miranda L. Barclay	Ricky Leung
Steve Barclay	T. Shawn Long
Aner Barriola	Ashley McIntyre
Naia Barriola	Maria Carmen O'Brien
Stephanie Barriola	Folashade Omisore
Eva Borsodi	Jennifer Stanley
Zoltan Borsodi	Nadja Vielot
Latasha Gerald	Fred Wyand

EDITED BY: Martha Kempner, MA
DESIGN BY: Sarah Gifford
PHOTOGRAPHY BY: Ricky Leung Photography

Printed in the United States of America

First Printing, 2014

ISBN 978-1-885833-00-6

American Sexual Health Association
PO Box 13827
Research Triangle Park, NC 27709
919.361.8400

www.ASHAsexualhealth.org
www.iwannaknow.org
www.quierosaber.org
www.NCCC-online.org